SEA-GIRT VIGIL

Sea-Girt Vigil

Alastair Christie-Johnston

The Shetland Times Ltd
Lerwick
2015

Sea-Girt Vigil

ISBN 978-1-904746-98-0

British Library Cataloguing-in-Publication Data.
A catalogue record of this book is available from the British Library.

Cover illustration from "The Monk by the Sea"
by Caspar David Friedrich (1774-1840).

Printed and published by
The Shetland Times Ltd.,
Gremista, Lerwick,
Shetland, Scotland. ZE1 0BW

For Zoe

SEA-GIRT VIGIL

Christianity arrived in Shetland around 500-600AD when the culture was predominantly Pictish. Small cells were established in many coastal regions, chosen for easy access from the sea and possibly for reasons of preferred solitude.

To this day the name "Papal" is repeated numerous times on Ordnance Survey maps, confirming the traditional recognition of these early Christian strongholds.

Many are on sea-girt rocks known locally as "birriers". One such birrier, on the island of Yell, is the main setting for this story.

Chapter I

Man shall not live by bread alone... **(Matt 4:4)**

When the keel ran in on the shingle we were all startled by the sudden harsh sound. It was as though a long vow of silence had been broken. Not that it had been so long. Three days. A propitious number for men of our calling. Three days of light winds and quiet seas since we had received the blessing of the Abbot of Orcades and kissed our newfound friends goodbye. Three days of futile attempts to divert fickle breezes into our heavy sail. Three days of back-breaking stints at the oars interspersed with queasy inactivity when thirst driven second thoughts led to introspection as we contemplated what the future held in store for us. And yet already I am being presumptuous as in truth I cannot speak for the others. Though they were my associates, I scarcely knew them.

It is always thus in religious communities such as ours. Or so I believe. We make a conscious decision to withdraw from the world and while we may live cheek by jowl with other like-minded men, our thoughts are all directed towards God and we are discouraged from forming intimate relationships with fellow ascetics. I can tell you the names of the others and describe their appearance but I know little else about them. Seven men sharing too little space in an open boat along with all their worldly goods; bound together on a mission to win souls for Christ and bound for Thule. Each one of us having blistered hands and cold feet. Each one of us wondering if this was folly beyond all folly. Thinking it in the silence that is our preferred companion. Not giving expression to the practicalities as worldly matters are of little consequence. Expressed thoughts are better reserved for higher things. Ecclesiastical debate. Hermeneutics. We were never short of a topic.

Our leader, or prior as he was properly termed, who sat in the prow of the boat with his back to us for most of the voyage, went by the name of Andreas. Father Andreas to his acolytes. His rugged face bore several scars and his nose appeared to have been broken at some time or other. He was powerfully built with thick cords of muscles in his arms and legs. I fancied he must have led a very different life before being re-born to this one. Whatever his beginnings may have been he was destined to lead and might as readily have led an army into battle as take on the precarious if laudable mission of bringing enlightenment to hitherto Godforsaken natives in a remote island beyond what was variously known in those days as Caledonia, Dail Riada, Alba or Cruithni, depending on your culture or political persuasion.

There was an underlying vitality and robustness in the prior's demeanour that seemed forever to be in conflict with the deific stoicism that characterised all his dealings with us. It was as if we were each a separate cross he had to bear and at times I truly believed he would have preferred to punch out my lights than to bestow unctuous benedictions upon my unruly head. For all my many failings he nevertheless continued to have faith in me and never once raised his voice in chastisement. It might have been better if he had. Better for me that is, if not for him.

Like so many others who sought to become Christ's disciples and follow the straight and narrow way that leads to eternal life, the prior's past was a closed book. He did not subscribe to the increasingly fashionable notion of making virtue out of one's miraculous rescue from depravity in order to prove the unsurpassed love of God. Some would have it the better Christian is he who has stooped so low as to have supped with the devil before being raised out of the pit to certain sainthood. Their testimonies are laced and traced with such debauchery as might be reckoned to make a listener's blood freeze in his veins. Only then may an audience be truly turned, their hearts warmed and their joy made complete when they discover how such a one has been saved to eternal life in a mansion surrounded by celestial choirs. To hear such testimonies one could be led to think that salvation depends upon first entering on a life of unspeakable sin: the greater the fall the greater the rise to glory, with the insinuated corollary that a man who has led an exemplary life is somehow a lesser Christian.

Whatever Father Andreas' past, he clearly did not believe anything was to be gained by flaunting it. Nor did I. As the son of devout and humble parents living in the comparatively peaceable island community of Mull where our forefathers had been early beneficiaries of the teachings of Columba's followers, I had been afforded few opportunities to do anything other than live a pious, albeit boring, life. My mother used to say companionable silence is preferable to idle chatter. She was never one for gossip and I suppose it set the tone for my love of quietness and peace.

I am aware many people feel uncomfortable when surrounded by silence and will begin coughing and clearing their throats as if this alone might ease the tension they perceive is taking a grip on the situation. They would do better to rise and leave the room. Go down to the sea and join its meaningless conversations with bubble-blowing crabs and loose living pebbles.

As a boy I craved adventure and if that is a sin then I suppose I must have been a sinner. Being also of a rather timid disposition I eventually compromised by going no further than across the narrow stretch of sea to Iona where I joined that island's monastic community at the tender age of 14. It was adventure of a sort. At least it was to begin with, though it soon became drudgery. Believe me, monastic life is no bed of roses! Yet I was lured and lulled by monotony. Drawn to the rock like a seal that seeks the same ledge on which to bask at every tide's turn, and like a rock-bound seal I learned the haunting songs and mantras that are designed to draw others into the mysteries of union, birth, death and everlasting life.

And now I have deviated from the path of my narrative (it is ever the way of those of my calling and explains why our sermons are so long). I was telling what little I know of the prior and the others. To the rest of us, six in all, Father Andreas was already an old man preparing himself for death. This would be his last mission – or so I believed. Why I had reached this conclusion I do not rightly know for in reality he could not have been above forty-five years of age. I fancy it was his world-weary countenance as compared with our fresh faces and eager spirits that caused me to think this way. Not one of us was above half our leader's age and the two novices, Cyrus and Stephanus, who joined us in Orcades, were mere boys who in wide-eyed innocence had pleaded with their superior to allow them to accompany us. Their enthusiasm had made me smile at the time because they used the word "adventure", much as I had a decade earlier when setting off for Iona. While granting their wish, the Abbot had drawn down his brows at such trivialising, expressly forbidding them to think in those terms.

"You are embarking on a mission of the greatest import," he stated in a voice calculated to strike awe into young hearts and minds. "It is God's will that you dedicate your lives to the task, nor ever think to lay down His sword until all evil is banished from those dark islands and they become bathed in His celestial light unto eternity and beyond."

Knowing that we were bound for Thule, which was generally believed to be within the compass of the Arctic Circle, I thought it a tall order. For at least six months of the year we might expect to see very little light and be obliged to endure long nights. And as everyone knows, darkness is the cloak of sin. The Devil is the Prince of Darkness, is he not?

Being scarcely ten years older than the boys I could well recall my own years as a novitiate when fear governed faith and I many times doubted my capacity to win through. I wondered how resolute they might be in the days ahead. I had benefitted from the supremely ordered life of a well-established monastic community whereas these babes in the woods were destined for uncertainty on barren rocks surrounded by uncharted seas. Even I, with a decade of discipline and training out of which I had learned some rudimentary Latin, gained a firm grasp on the Gospel message and been elevated to the status of priest; even I was more than a little afraid. Of the other three, I can only speak in general terms of my associate and fellow-traveller, John, who had shared a cell with me on Iona and agreed to join me on this latest venture. He too was a priest.

It should be understood that despite the isolation of the many monastic communities throughout Britain and the cloistered existence of those who dwell within their walls, there exists an astonishing network of communications. If the spider at the centre of the web (by which I mean His Holiness, the Pope) should happen to genuflect, we all sense the spirituality and promptly do likewise. Apart from anything else it is important that we conform to a commonality that ensures strength of purpose. There is but one God. There are schisms. I do not deny it. And there are varying creeds and dogmas that threaten the very fabric of the Church, yet we strive to present a united front. When setting forth to spread the Gospel we try, in as far as we are able, to utilise our limited manpower to best effect and avoid treading on one another's toes.

Thus it came about, when a mission was requested by the central ecclesiastical authority in Thule to plant a cell on the one remaining island that had so far been overlooked, that request was heard in every corner of the land and even in far off Rome. It came as no surprise to learn that the island of perceived need was named Gjall (meaning "barren")[1] suggesting reason enough for leaving it until last. It did not inspire much confidence in our little band of missionaries to believe we might succeed in turning barrenness into fertility, let alone grow anything of worth – never mind the numerous Biblical precedents for doing so.

The other two in our little crew were both from the Northumbria monastery of Whithorn which had been founded by Ninian towards the middle of the 4th century and some 200 years before our time. Their names were Leon and Maccus and like John and me, they were also ordained priests. Aside from the novices and our venerable leader, we four priests were of similar age and

---

[1] All place-names within Thule are Old Norse, which very probably was introduced at a later period to that of the narrative; however, in the absence of any recorded Pictish alternatives, I must beg the reader's indulgence.

appearance. All in our mid-twenties and all under-nourished, we were lean and gaunt. Each of us wore the innately pious visage one associates with monks. It was the mien we were encouraged to adopt; it being assumed outward appearance is a window to inner thoughts. We might easily have passed for brothers and indeed only addressed one another as such. All four of us wore long cloaks.

Though woven on different looms by different hands our garments were nevertheless uniformly crafted out of homespun cloth. All were seamless according to a tradition which decreed that monks be clad in similar attire to that worn by our Lord on the day of his crucifixion. Other than this our wardrobes were sparse. Grey woollen breeches, a short tunic, linen undergarments and leather sandals. Anything else was considered superfluous although socks were worn in winter. Yet we were generally better clad than the poor we claimed to serve. Better fed too. Even chieftains and their entourages did not eat as well as we did, and this because our monastic communities were largely made up of educated men, skilled agriculturalists and artisans. Unlike the ignorant poor, we knew how to make the most of what we had. Yet it should not be supposed that as individuals we were greedy. A few were, it cannot be denied, but the community as a whole nurtured itself well by pooling resources and capitalising on good husbandry. When alone however we were quite the opposite and it must be remembered that first and foremost a monk of whatever order or persuasion always seeks solitude over company and from time to time will withdraw for extended periods of self-imposed deprivation in order to meditate, muse upon and commune with God. For my part it was the prospect of this special kind of retreat that had caused me to seek the thinly populated islands of Thule.

By comparison, the reason Leon and Maccus had sought to be part of the mission was the promise of an opportunity to set foot on St Ninian's Isle which was currently the seat of the Abbot of Thule. Ninian was their patron saint and while there was no evidence of his ever having visited the island, it meant a great deal to them that it was named after him. For them the mission was a pilgrimage of sorts. Indeed it was on the shore of this very island that we were now about to disembark and the Whithorn pair could hardly contain their excitement.

In his eagerness Leon kilted his robe and leapt overboard from the stern of our boat, landing (if one can land) in four feet of water, thereby soaking half his clothing. Before he could wade to the bow and haul the boat further up the shingle, a voice hailed us from the cliff-top and to the accompaniment of much gesticulating we were directed to row further along the coast to where a sort of hollow or shallow trench had been dug into a sandy tombolo, making it possible to step ashore dry shod. Immediately above this spot on a grassy promontory several thatch-roofed stone huts surrounded a slightly larger building before which a granite Celtic cross gave testimony to Christian occupation. The entire island was treeless, making the cross the highest object in the landscape. There could be no escaping its message of dominance. The crucified Christ had come to this place and He held sway over all else.

Chapter II

*Better a stupid and unlettered brother who, working the good things
he knows, merits life in heaven than one who though being
distinguished for his learning in the Scriptures, or even holding the
place of a doctor, lacks the bread of love* (St Bede, the Venerable)

A mass was held to celebrate our safe arrival, which being at
noon was offered during Sext when the 23rd Psalm was read
and prayers offered for our mission. We were then given a
somewhat frugal meal comprising of shellfish and gruel. We were
grateful nonetheless. The weather was fair and we were safely
arrived. Some of the local monks kindly vacated one of their
beehive-shaped huts in order that we might have a place to sleep on
our first night. Not that we were encouraged to think such an
arrangement might pertain for any length of time. In fact the Abbot
(who happened to be in residence at the time) made it clear that we
would have to proceed on our way the following morning. We were
to leave the boat and travel overland to the east coast from where we
would once again proceed by sea; going north to the island of Gjall.
We were to be loaned the use of a pony to help carry our
possessions and a guide would accompany us as far as Leirvik, in
which place we would meet with other monks and be provided with
a boat and chart. In monastic life, owning everything in common
has much to commend it.

Tired though I was, I decided to explore St Ninian's Isle before
going to bed. It was the month of May which meant daylight
lingered in the sky for most of the night in a sort of perpetual
twilight in which the sun was never far below the horizon. If I
needed to be enchanted into falling in love with Thule there could
be no better Island and no better night on which to do so. It was the
avian breeding season and as I crossed the high ground making for

the far side of the island the sky seemed to be full of anxious birds. It almost made me turn back as I had no wish to disturb them needlessly. Then, as suddenly as they appeared, they seemed to sense that I meant them no harm and within the space of a few moments they ceased their clamour and sloped off down invisible air currents to resume copulation, incubation, or whatever else they were previously engaged upon. The air positively hummed with the business of making new life and wherever I trod, the grass and moss refused to remain bent or crushed under my feet, springing back with renewed vigour to worshipfully follow in the sun's path.

I was well aware of the danger of worshipping nature in lieu of God, or of reverting to paganism in the form of unholy deities – Pan, Bacchus and the multitudinous array of gods and goddesses of flowers, fruit and fertility. Too easily one could be lured away down an Elysian path in pursuit of hedonistic delights. Too often I had been tempted to step that way, turning, not a moment too soon, to the Psalmist for rescue. And whenever I found myself in this frame of mind, I focussed once more on my primary goal in life; my desire to see God more clearly, love Him more dearly and follow Him more nearly.

I had discussed this briefly with both John and our prior, John being of like-mind and Father Andreas keen that we both find fulfilment. Every monk who volunteered to embark upon a period of solitary isolation, whether for a week or a month, was assured of the full support of his abbot or prior in order to counteract the laity's perception that monasteries and monks' cells are places of soft living. Moreover it was thought desirable that a man who truly wished to attain holiness should seek his God by this means. We all subscribed to the notion of forty days and forty nights in the wilderness, however impractical and untenable the idea might be. We all knew chapter and verse of our Lord's ordeal and even joked about the brevity of Matthew's words.

And when he had fasted forty days and forty nights, he was afterwards an hungered. No hyperbole there. It had to be the classic understatement of all time. And in the ensuing half millennium the Church had come to realise that no man could actually survive a fast that extended over such a long period without God's miraculous intervention. Few had lived beyond twenty days and then only if they had entered upon the period of self-denial in a state of extreme fitness and preferably with a healthy layer of fat round their bellies. Even so, the environment in which the hermit chose to spend his time in lone meditation could not be too Spartan and the weather would need to be kind.

Little wonder so many died, especially as everyone who embarked upon such a venture felt obliged to make it as miserable as possible. In the absence of desert wilderness such as Jesus endured, the next best (or worst) option seemed to be barren rocks lashed by winter's storms, or failing that, a windswept mountain-top.

And I was no different. It was a matter of principle that I seek the worst possible site in which to sit out my self-imposed muse. One who declared himself to be a disciple of the Lord must surely be prepared to endure in equal measure what his brother had endured. And if it required a miracle in order to achieve such endurance then God's will be done. For whereas I firmly believe that monasteries provide opportunity in which to absorb the collective learning of the Church and enter into spiritual communion with like-minded souls, only through deprivation in lonely exile can one ever expect to meet God and hear the still small voice of truth.

In those first few years in Iona I swiftly learned the veracity of this, sometimes leaving the community and crossing the island to the bleak west coast where only rocks stand defiant against the marauding onslaught of a never-tiring sea. Though I seldom stayed for more than a day or two at a time, it was enough to realise that a hitherto unplumbed depth of fortitude would need to be called upon if I was to survive much longer. I would need to become a rock among rocks; an inanimate object devoid of all feeling, immune to heat and cold alike. I would need stoicism and tenacity in abundance. I might crack, as a rock will crack in extreme circumstances, yet I must not sunder or all would be lost and I would become shifting sand. Could I endure, and if so for how long? More to the point, would I discover the essence of God at the core of my endurance?

Thule was to be my testing ground and I had chosen it in the belief that only the most ardent follower of Christ would go to such lengths to escape the devil and find salvation. For escaping the devil was a vital part of the equation as no one need expect to be able to resist his temptations in the manner of our Lord. My only hope was to find a place as fraught with deprivation and misery as to be less than appealing to Satan who, after all, prefers the world's fleshpots. Not that I imagined I could wholly escape him. He would surely come. My salvation (if salvation was to be granted) would depend on the devil being disinclined to hang around too long. In other words I must find a place that was so unspeakably desolate that even the devil would shun it.

In truth we monks have an unhealthy preoccupation with the devil, seeing him in all manner of things that might more readily be associated with the creator. Almost half our time seems to be given to supposedly resisting Satan when we would do better to simply turn our backs and focus on loftier things. The devil is in the detail, or so they say and we promptly go looking for him as if by doing so we might expunge him. Yet every moment spent with the devil is a moment in which we move further away from God. These sorts of thoughts troubled me when I realised I might find the perfect place in which to commune with God only to become preoccupied with devilish thoughts. It was a veritable conundrum to which I would only find the solution when eventually faced with the situation. Meanwhile I must engage the virtue of patience. When I returned to the monastery it was well past midnight. A candle burned in the chapel and I slipped in to hear Vigils being read before retiring for the night.

The following day dawned at an unspeakably early hour and we were about our business at what I might in other circumstances have called an ungodly hour. Yet, for monks, there are no ungodly hours. Sometime in the previous evening (probably when I was away exploring the island) Leon and Maccus had sought and been granted permission to remain as part of the St Ninian's Isle community and in their place our designated guide, Thomas, was to continue with us to Gjall. The pony we were being loaned would be got back by some other means.

I had come to quite like Leon who appeared to have a lively and enquiring mind and found myself hoping his replacement would not exhibit any of his namesake's characteristics. Bad enough that we should now be a man short without his replacement being one given to reservations and misgivings. Fortunately Thomas was more of an age with our prior and therefore might prove to be a good companion for him. Like Leon and Maccus, Father Andreas came from Whithorn which was reputed to be a seat of great learning. Father Andreas' reputation as a saintly man had been further enhanced by his having travelled to Rome where he met His Holiness, The Pope and received his blessing. This alone was reckoned to give a man an aura of sanctity. It might therefore be supposed if Thomas had any doubts regarding his faith, they would soon be dispelled through association with our good and Godly prior. John and I were more or less kindred spirits and the novices had time on their side. Meanwhile they could look out for themselves. As the Abbot of Iona was wont to say *Deo adjuvante non timendum.* By the grace of God it would all work out for the best; or words to that effect.

After another meal of gruel we set out on our overland journey with Father Andreas wondering if it might be deemed cruelty to animals to have added our heavy iron cooking pot to the diminutive pony's load. I looked at the shaggy little creature with its big brown eyes and sturdy legs. It was barely half an arm-span high and I was put in mind of a story (most probably apocryphal) that my father used to tell of how he once met a portly farmer sitting astride a similarly sized beast with his feet practically touching the ground. My father admonished the lazy-looking fellow for what he perceived to be cruelty, only to be informed "Na, na laddie, you have it all wrong. Whiles he carries me and whiles I carries him."

Noting that the pony's name was Atlas I presumed he could cope well enough with the load. Nevertheless I promised to remove the pot and carry it myself if the animal began lagging.

As yet we had not met any natives although Thomas assured us we would in all probability do so on the way to Leirvik. The folk were predominantly Picts and Gaels who apparently favoured the interior of the islands over the coastal regions, frequenting the more wooded valleys and lower slopes of the hills. These were people with whom I was acquainted and with whom I could converse – particularly the Gaels. Even though they too were a warring people, they were of my own blood. It bode well for our mission.

First things first however. We had yet to establish a base, find a source of food and build adequate shelter. Much work needed to be done before winter storms beset us. We would need to obtain some livestock. A cow or goat. Some sheep which were to be kept for wool only as we did not eat meat other than poultry and fish. A dog would be companionable. We had limited skills, or so I thought; not knowing anything of Thomas nor yet of the novices whose ingenuity would soon amaze me. Father Andreas, ancient as I had first supposed him to be, would also prove to be a tower of strength, and a man of many parts. John had been a coast-dweller; a fisherman. I hoped he might build us a coracle and harvest the sea. He knew little of animal husbandry nor yet of agriculture. He had a gift of healing, however. I had helped my father build walls and byres and I knew one or two other useful things including how to cook. Doubtless we would all find our niche.

As we began trudging eastward, each of us laden with the trappings of survival, I thought about all that had gone before in my life and wondered what was to become of me in this new phase. My shoulders were already beginning to ache under the weight of my possessions which included a few books that were to be the nucleus of our library. Oh, yes; our scraps of writings! They were our stock-in-trade. We were nothing without them. *I* was nothing without them. And yet they goaded me now as if to mock my piety. Awkward, angular shapes wrapped in canvas; the hard corners gouging between my shoulder-blades making me wince at every step.

I had my Biblical texts, of course; much handled and soiled though they were. Very few individual monks owned complete Bibles, most belonging to monastery libraries. I also had a battered copy of Augustine's *Confession on Christian Doctrine* given to me by the Iona Sacristan as a parting gift. (The Iona Community adhered to Augustine's teachings and rejected Donatism and the Arian beliefs, confessing the equality of the triune God, Father, Son and Holy Ghost, one and the same.) I had other textual fragments too. Mere words, all of them. Dry on drier parchment. Dry as dust. Artfully illuminated texts now fading and becoming discoloured. I might read them till my eyes dimmed and still not discover the true God. Had I not many times observed other monks seeking the same truths, hunched over their desks under narrow leaded windows where dust motes vacillated in sunlit shafts that gave light without enlightenment? I many times questioned them, asking if they had found anything new. They could not say yea or nay, or if they could they preferred not to until the last iota of dust settled and all became clear as crystal. And when would that be?

Yet if God was not to be revealed in the written word then where might I find Him? Surely the Gospels, if not the words of the prophets, contained elements of the truth. If only they had presented a united front when first they set about recording it all. Their mismatched accounts raised more questions than they answered. It was all a great mystery and more to the point a galling burden. I wondered at the wisdom of putting so much faith in books when in truth God was all about me; winking out of a shiny leaf or leading me in green pastures, as the psalmist would have it. And to think I had offered to share the portage of that confounded pot with the pony! I prayed it would prove unnecessary. "Give strength to the pony's back, O Lord, and remove the ache from mine".

He wasn't listening.   Or perhaps he was.

Thomas came up and walked beside me, taking one of the heavier packages when he saw my bent back and sweated brow. He turned out to be something of a chatterbox which further distracted me from my woes. He had lived much of his life in the highlands of what he called Cruithni where his father was a shepherd. As a boy he had roamed the hills and valleys discovering the secretive ways of beaver, wild boar, deer, bears and the eagle. He became both a hunter and a protector. And when the menfolk of the valley gathered together on winter evenings, he sat unseen in the shadows of the chimney neuk listening to tall tales and watching the way in which they fashioned and repaired their tools of trade, thereby learning many useful things. For it is possible to learn much about life in this way. Skills require practise, it is true, yet they are begun by watching and listening. And so I listened to Thomas as the miles passed under our feet.

"I didn't catch your name when introductions were being made yestere'en," he said at one point.

"Somhairle," I replied.

"Ah! A good choice for a man who hopes to meet his God."

It was commonplace for men to change their names and choose a Christian one at conversion or baptism and I presumed Thomas thought this was so in my case.

"It was my parents' choice, not mine," I explained. "They are Christians also and named me at birth. My mother wished that by so naming me I might hear God's voice."

"And have you?"

I smiled, knowing he would not expect an affirmative reply. Miracles still happened though they were generally confined to healings and visions of angels. To the best of my knowledge no one had seen or heard God for a long time and what accounts there were appeared to be shrouded in ambiguity.

"Not in so many words," I said. "I have not given up however. I mean to embark upon a period of solitary meditation as soon as is it becomes feasible to do so. It is my chief reason for coming here."

This revelation seemed to give Thomas cause to ponder. He said nothing more for a while and we continued walking in silence. I was keeping a sharp lookout for a first glimpse of any natives while also observing the countryside through which we were travelling. Most of the shrubbery was stunted and blasted by the wind. By all accounts it blew more or less incessantly and with such ferocity as was seldom experienced further south. Not on this day, God be praised. On this day the weather was kind. The sun shone out of a blue sky and everything that could sparkle was delighted to do so.

After about an hour or so we came upon a family group sitting round a fire. A dark-hair boy was turning a spit on which a small animal was skewered. It looked like a rabbit but may have been a pine martin or some other creature unknown to me. Whatever it was it smelled ambrosial – most definitely worthy of the gods. It set my mouth watering. I had not eaten flesh of any sort for some days and could happily have devoured the lot. Nor would conscience have got in the way. Then I looked again at the ragged group and silently begged their forgiveness for allowing my gluttony to momentarily rule my heart. For all that I would have given an eye tooth for a morsel; I could clearly see their need was greater than mine. Four skinny children and a sad-eyed mother. No sign of a man. What untold story lay behind that scene?

We each made an offering as we passed by. Stephanus and Cyrus gave some salt fish left over from provisions brought from Orcades. John and I gave coin and Thomas a small skin of goat's cheese he had been looking forward to enjoying at suppertime.

Father Andreas gave his blessing and who is to say he did not give the greater gift? Not I. The food would last a day, two at the most. The blessing, with God's grace, would last a lifetime.

It was a matter of principle within our communities that we always sought to alleviate poverty, giving alms whenever the need arose. The danger of living in cloistered surroundings meant we did not habitually confront poverty and might easily come to believe it did not exist. This tended to be the case on Iona and most probably in many other of our isolated communities as well. It could even be argued that we deliberately shut ourselves off in order to avoid confronting what we did not wish to see. I admit it was true in my case. I heard the Bible's teachings and conveniently concluded they did not apply to me. This changed however when I travelled through the country on my way to Orcades. John and I were equally shocked by what we saw and agreed we must seek to make amends or risk God's judgement. Our ambition to enter upon a time of reflective isolation would have to be balanced by subsequent servitude. We would have to seek out the poor and assist them in every way possible – not through alms alone but by teaching skills and habits which would lead to self-sufficiency. Our mission was to be twofold. We were committed to making it work.

A short while later we were overtaken by a man leading a goat. He was a swarthy looking fellow with a thick beard and deep-set greenish eyes. He wore a long tunic and breeches made of moleskin or something similar. His shoes were of pigskin. He greeted us with a nod and made to pass by then thought better of it. I could see he was in two minds about something.

"Are ye bound for Leirvik?" he asked in a guttural voice. It was a relief to discover he spoke our language although I soon came to realise, after entering into conversation with him, that his vocabulary included many words I had never heard before. The accent and cadence differed markedly to the lilt of the western isles where folk spoke as if about to break into song.

When it was established that we were indeed going to the village the man enquired if we would like to buy his goat which he was taking there to sell. Thereupon we entered into negotiations, particularly as we could see it was a nanny and that she was in milk.

Her kid had died, the man explained and he needed the money. Fortunately for us, Thomas knew a thing or two about goats and judged the beast to be healthy. He looked at her teeth and declared her to be two-year old. A good buy, so he said; though not within hearing of the seller. It didn't do to appear too naïve. When it came to driving a bargain, Father Andreas was our man. He spoke with the authority of one who knew how many beans made five, and he was not above using a little intimidation where it might help close the deal.

"We are doing you a service, taking the beast off your hands," he declared. "Why, you might walk all the way to village only to find no buyer. And you may be assured we will treat the animal kindly."

I thought it unlikely the man could have cared one way or another how we treated his goat and supposed he'd be more than happy to be rid of it. He looked to be a coarse sort of a fellow. Yet looks can be misleading and I should not judge lest I be judged in turn. In any event the deal was made and we continued on our way, a little lighter in our communal purse and the proud owners of a nanny goat called Miriam – according to Stephanus.

"Why Miriam?" I queried.

"Because it is the name she gave when I asked her," he replied.

"It's true," Cyrus added.

"Yes, I can see it might be," I said and we all laughed heartily.

We reached Leirvik shortly after noon. It was a somewhat disappointing scene that confronted us when we topped the hill overlooking the area. I speak not of the view, which was pleasing enough, but rather of the village. To my way of thinking it was no village at all. When I expressed this opinion Thomas explained that the main settlement in the islands lay some miles to the west and Leirvik was a secondary affair of minor consequence.

"The district takes its name from clay deposits which are used for making pots and jars. Otherwise it is a good place for landing fish and has a market," he explained.

"And where are the monks? I see no monastery," John declared, raising a quizzical eyebrow.

Thomas smiled.

"You see well, brother. We have no monasteries in Thule – yet. Nor do the monks live in the village yonder. It is a rough place by all accounts. Our brothers live on the island across the bay."

"And how do we get there?" I asked, noting what appeared to be impenetrable cliffs facing us from about a mile across the sea.

"We go down through the village and out to the north. See. There is a narrow channel at that point. From there we can signal. There is a flagpole on the shore for the purpose. They will send a boat for us when the tide is right. Come, let's go. I'm starving!"

Thomas was clearly a man of action.

But Father Andreas was not to be hurried and I fancied he felt a need to reclaim his leadership.

"Wait," he said, stepping aside from the path to sit on a large rock. "I wish to make a sketch. We will pause and eat some lunch."

I gratefully lowered my several packages to the ground, as did the others. Cyrus tethered the goat on a patch of grass while

Stephanus tied up the pony. We then set about pooling what items of food we had among us. It turned out to be very little indeed. John contributed a few small barley loaves which the Ninian's Isle monks had given him and the boys produced the remains of the dried fish. It was not enough to feed six hungry mouths. Stephanus fetched a pannikin of water from a nearby pool and after the prior had said a blessing we set too as if it were a feast and the water was finest wine.

The fish was tough as an old boot and tasted of nothing other than salt. I spat out a bone and cast my mind back to the spit-roasted rabbit, fancying I could still smell the crisp outer flesh and taste the succulent juices flowing down the back of my throat. I closed my eyes, gnawing on the hard fish while pretending I sat in a banquet hall where a platter of steaming meat oozing rich gravy had been placed before me. A goblet filled to the brim with ruby-red wine stood at my right hand. I felt a smile creeping out from the corners of my mouth. I opened my eyes and looked at the others. They were all smiling too as they munched on the miserable repast. All fantasising, as I was. It was a miracle. Or it was a joke. I am not sure which.

After our meal we sat awhile, waiting for the prior to complete his sketch which he was executing on a scrap of linen with charcoal. And I must admit the view was worthy of artistic endeavour. Low islands stretched for as far as the eye could see. Greens, russets, brown of every hue with the sea insinuating its sparkling presence between them all. A skylark was singing in the firmament. Somewhere in the grass at our feet a cup-shaped nest would contain the first egg of a new season. Blue as the sky.

The monk's isle (I later heard it was named Brei Oy) dominated the skyline, having a steep-sided hill that rose to a height of what I guessed to be about 600 feet. The prior's sketch made it look higher. A bank of cloud was approaching from the east and when I tactfully pointed it out; Father Andreas packed away his crayons and declared it was time to move on.

Chapter III

*Men go abroad to wonder at the heights of mountains, at the huge
waves of the sea, at the long courses of the rivers, at the vast compass of
the ocean, at the circular motion of the stars, and they pass by
themselves without wondering.* **(St Augustine)**

We walked down the slope and through the village, keeping a
sharp lookout for any ruffians who might attempt to molest
us. For some reason monks were thought to have fat purses and to
be easy prey. The villains were wrong on both counts. We seldom
had two pennies to rub together and most of us could wield a staff
to good effect when called upon to defend ourselves. As it
happened, few paid us any heed. It appeared the populace were
becoming used to seeing monks and in our case Miriam, trotting
along beside us, seemed to lend an air of respectability and innocent
domesticity to our little party. We passed the marketplace to which
presumably Miriam had originally been destined. It looked to be
lively enough and it occurred to me the seller might have done
better to complete his journey. Then again, he may have been
tempted to turn aside into one of the several taverns and ended up
the poorer before returning home. Indeed, when a whiff of hops
reached my nostrils and I saw two men sitting against a wall
enjoying tankards of ale, I was tempted to turn aside myself and said
as much to John. He shook his head.

"We might miss the tide and be stranded on a cold shore. I fancy
a square meal and a bed, in that order. My feet are killing me."

For the most part the populace looked healthy and to be of
modest means. I saw no beggars such as were commonplace in
other villages I had passed through. The children ran barefooted and
ragged, yet they laughed and skipped. No voice was raised. No one

scolded. It appeared Thomas' assessment of the village being a "rough place" might have been a trifle harsh.

As we continued northwards I noticed a young black and tan collie had attached itself to our party, roaming from side to side as if we were a flock of sheep that needed to be kept together. From time to time he made a feint at the goat which trotted on with its head held high, paying no heed. Though one or other of us ordered the dog home from time to time, it pretended not to understand, cocking an ear and standing with one paw raised as if begging forgiveness for being so stupid.

When we came to the flagpole the tide was full and had ceased to flow. Thomas ran a piece of cloth up the mast and immediately a boat pulled away from the opposite shore. It was not above two furlongs across. It seemed word had reached them and they knew we were coming, though how that could be I have no idea.

The boat was broad-beamed and large. A sea-going craft if ever I saw one. Two men sat amidships pulling an oar apiece while a third stood in the bow holding a length of rope which he threw to us as they came alongside the small jetty upon which we were waiting.

The men greeted us warmly and we quickly set about loading our possessions. Miriam did not seem to mind being lifted on board where she stood athwart the scuppers staring intently at the sea as if contemplating its substance. Meanwhile the third member of the crew, who turned out to be a novice of similar age to our boys, took charge of the pony and immediately set off on the return journey to St Ninian's Isle.

While we were all busily engaged in getting on board the dog bounded joyfully over the stern to land in John's lap.

"Put that dog back on the shore," the prior told Cyrus. "Send it home. Someone must own it and be wondering where it has got to."

Cyrus did as he was bid, shooing the animal half-heartedly and no doubt secretly hoping it would not go as it was patently obvious the boy had fallen in love with it. The dog barked in protest, leaping into the sea and swimming after us as soon as we pulled away.

"He'll drown," Cyrus wailed, even though the dog looked perfectly capable of swimming across the narrow waterway with ease.

Father Andreas sighed audibly.

"Very well, help it aboard but have a care, you are rocking the boat."

And in this manner Argos came into our lives; named for his unflagging faithfulness. Both our novices were delighted.

By the time we reached the island the fog I had seen out to sea was beginning to roll in from the east while behind us the sun still shone brightly. The two boatmen were anxious that we not delay as their dwellings lay about a mile across the hill. With two extra helpers to carry our chattels we made good progress and were soon in sight of a small cluster of stone huts near the north-east corner of the island. The huts were some of the best I had seen of the type. This was largely due to a fine quality of sandstone that was being quarried nearby. It appeared the community was also blessed with a skilled stonemason. Lucky for some, I thought, never guessing that this man would shortly offer his services to help establish us on Gjall.

In the course of the evening and over an excellent meal that included grilled fish followed by cheese, bread and wine, we learned that all the religious communities regularly visited one another and interchanged labour according to differing needs and stages of development. We were to be given loan of a boat to go Gjall in a day or so, depending on the weather. A party of carpenters and stonemasons would travel north a few weeks later to help establish our base once we had chosen a suitable site. They would then bring the loaned boat back, possibly leaving us a smaller one for purposes of in-shore fishing and more localised travel. Father Andreas spoke up, thanking our hosts for their generous offers of help and assuring them we would return the favour in whatever way we could.

I had spoken with John about my idea of building a coracle and he now expressed the hope that he might find time to do so later in the year when the days were shorter and other projects were likely to be curtailed.

"We will be grateful for the temporary use of a little boat," he said. "But I believe we should all strive for self-sufficiency and it is my plan to build a coracle before year's end."

This brought nods of approval from the gathering and others began speaking of their own goals. It was clear to me that however much everyone spoke of communal enterprise we were individualists at heart and in the midst of it all I began wondering how and when I was going to achieve my ambition to pursue true monasticism which after all implied living alone. I was eager to find my rock, my eyrie on which to perch and begin the search for spiritual enlightenment. I do not recall giving expression to my thoughts, however I found myself in conversation with one of the local monks; another gaunt fellow with protruding cheek bones, a Roman nose and brown Mediterranean eyes who asked me if I would like to visit their hermitage site on the southern cliffs.

"You don't mean those high cliffs we saw from the other side," I said in disbelief. "How could one possibly survive up there?"

"Come with me in the morning and I'll show you," he said.

As on St Ninian's Isle, we were given a hut to ourselves, excepting on this occasion no one was required to vacate it due to some of the community having gone to yet another island to help with ploughing and seeding. We all retired shortly after Compline. Sea-fog had chilled the air and the warmest place was reckoned to be our cots. Besides, it had been a long day.

In the morning the weather deteriorated further. Fog turned to drizzle as the wind picked up, driving a chill into the core of my marrow. Being prone to rheumatics meant weather of this sort was the very devil as far as I was concerned. I thought it unlikely we would be making an excursion to the cliffs. It would surely be too dangerous. Imagine my surprise when my companion of the previous evening arrived to escort me before I had risen. His name was Jacob.

"Hurry up," he said. We have a piece to walk and I'm hoping for some gulls eggs for breakfast."

Horror of horrors! We were to travel on our fasted stomachs. The thought prompted me to realise I was becoming soft. And to think I hankered after a *real* fast. Merciful God, protect me from folly.

It was a two mile walk to the south end of the island. We skirted the high hill, keeping to the west coast until reaching the slope leading to the cliff top. It was a steep pinch and slippery in parts, as I had predicted. Yet on we clambered, wet to the skin. Madness, you might say. Somewhere on this wind-swept precipice a lone monk was sitting in penance for his sins. The least we could do was bring him a little cheer (and a small piece of goat's cheese I'd seen Jacob take from the larder before we set out).

When we reached the dizzy summit, our heads in cloud and the sea hidden from sight far below, I looked in vain for a cell of any sort. There was nothing but the blasted moor. Jacob beckoned me to join him at the cliff edge where clumps of thrift were beginning to bloom in defiance of the worst the sky could throw at it. Never one for heights, I approached in some trepidation. When looking at these same cliffs on the previous day I had estimated them to be in the order of 600 feet high. A long way to fall.

"It's perfectly safe. Come and look."

Reaching the edge I peered over and to my surprise there was a steep grassy slope ending in a sort of narrow plateau about fifty feet below on which some sheep were grazing.

"It is sheer to the sea on the other side of that," Jacob explained. "But the ledge is safe as houses and less exposed than you might imagine. The contrary air currents one always finds at cliff-tops are dissipated down there to form a sort of refuge into which the wind hardly goes. Added to which, because we are facing south, this little eyrie captures every ray of sunshine that the heavens afford; a particular consideration in winter, I assure you." He pointed to a spot directly below us. "Amongst those larger rocks you see near the edge, we have built as snug a cell as one might hope to find anywhere. Come, I'll show you."

Down we went, following a well-worn path that snaked through coarse tufts of grass where bumble bees hummed amongst sweet-scented wildflowers. And sure enough, as soon as we were off the ridge the wind left us alone. The further down we went the warmer it became. Even the persistent drizzle seemed to be driven out of the hollow and I judged the place to be a pocket-paradise. It was a foolish thought when I came to realise it would not always be so. There had to be days when banshee gales were not to be thwarted and others when deep drifts of snow would be driven here to fill the hollow and freeze blood in the veins of every living thing. Winters would be especially cruel when long dark nights brought doubt and fear creeping out from under every stone. I imagined the sea moaning and crashing in caves far below where the spirits of drowned seamen shrieked when the Devil came for them. Every vigil would seem to last an eternity. Every new day would bring fresh uncertainties to test faith.

Crossing the narrow sward to where we could see the thatched roof of a tiny round cell, Jacob cried out "*Deus tecum.*" Immediately a bearded face appeared above the stonework.

"*Benedictus, qui venit in nomine Domini,*" came the reply.

Jacob and the hermit embraced then I was introduced and embraced likewise. It was not an altogether joyous experience as the man smelled none too fresh, despite existing in the freshest air in the world. He was the strong silent type, or else prolonged loneliness had taken his tongue – excepting a string of Old Testament texts he poured out from time to time. All were in Latin, of course, as we did not quote the sacred words in our own language. And I use the word strong advisedly because the man lifted a huge rock and hurled it over the cliff in order to demonstrate that he remained hale despite having already spent fifteen days alone, presumably with very little to eat – unless he was devouring the sheep one by one.

I found the answer to my unspoken question when peeping into the hut (holding my nose as I did so). On a rock shelf stood a bowl of gulls' eggs which Jacob explained were eaten raw. The method of doing so involved drilling a hole in either end with a sharp splinter and then sucking out the contents. It was bound to be an excellent, if monotonous diet and something to remember when I set about my own retreat; supposing it might likewise be in the nesting season.

Another thing I learned that day was the manner in which the monks collected eggs, and here I speak not of the dangerous business of descending cliffs on a rush rope and a prayer. Rather I speak of the thoughtful way individual nests were marked and watched. Once a first egg was laid it was left until a second appeared, after which it and a third were taken and the fourth left. This allowed the breeding pair to raise two chicks. Such husbandry meant no bird was deprived of its God-given right to breed and moreover the resulting chicks were generally reckoned to be fatter and healthier than those in the un-robbed nests of their cousins. When compared to the indiscriminate wholesale plunder others engaged in, my brother monks in Thule claimed they always served God first. I resolved, wherever possible, to do likewise.

The hermit offered us his bowl of eggs in exchange for the cheese Jacob had brought, thereby postponing my first terrifying experience on the end of a rope. Thereafter it was a recurring nightmare I began having and one I fully expected to confront open-eyed at some time in the future. My life might depend on it; or my death. Meanwhile I baulked at sucking raw eggs to break my fast and suggested we take them back to the community where we could share ... and cook them.

We left the Brei Oy hermit who continued shouting texts until we were out of earshot – and all day long for all I know. I thought he might be a little unhinged and wondered if the same would happen to me when my time came. The drizzle met us on the summit and escorted us back through the sodden isle. When we reached the community I was ready to drop from exhaustion brought on by hunger.

All the talk now was of us leaving for Gjall as soon as weather permitted. Father Andreas was eager to establish a monastic site in his own name and the rest of us were right behind him. In this regard we were somewhat surprised to learn we were not going to be the first Christians to make landfall on the island as another group had beat us to it by several weeks. It would turn out to be a blessing in disguise as the others had chosen to go north to the bleaker end of the island, leaving us to colonise the south where we could expect better exposure to the all-important sun during the winter solstice.

Word had it the island was sparsely populated meaning conversion of the natives was likely to be secondary to establishing a strategic link with neighbouring cells. It should be understood, making the Church's universal mission work was all about reinforcing the web that bound us together. Every additional cell strengthened the fabric and ensured the faith was proclaimed abroad. There were to be no dark corners in which paganism might continue to flourish. Not even a shadow of doubt must remain. Light and right would prevail and to this end a presence was what mattered first and foremost. Once the torch had been lit in every district the natives would come as moths to a flame. They would submit to the light, become scorched out of their old ways and be reborn to purity.

The next day brought perfect conditions. A fresh south-easterly breeze promised to fill our sail and the sea was once again sparkling in anticipation of carrying us north on its serried waves. Everyone set to with a will and the boat was soon loaded. Miriam and Argos had become firm friends and lay peaceably under the stern thwart, wedged in with assorted baggage. The Brei Oy monks generously supplied us with extra provisions including a quantity of sheep's milk cheese, a sack of oatmeal and some much needed tools with which to begin building our new homes. They promised to visit us within a half moon, giving us time to explore the island and choose a suitable base. The consensus was that we should confine ourselves to the southern half of the island after first making a tour and visiting the monks in the north who, word had it, were already busily building on a promontory where high dunes afforded shelter behind a wide curve of sand.

In all the discussion we had before departing Brei Oy, I was amazed to discover the extent to which the various cells interacted with one another. The sea was a busy road over which men sailed from island to island, bringing news and offering assistance to one another. Far from operating in isolation, a powerful sense of oneness prevailed. It was something I would increasingly feel proud to be a part of.

Chapter IV

Deus providebit
(God will provide)

L eaving our new friends waving on the shore we soon caught a
strong current running up the coast of the mainland and passed
several small islands to starboard. The wind added its help, sending
us spanking along in high spirits. John had taken the tiller, as he
generally did whenever we went to sea, and as little was needed in
the way of the oars it meant the rest of us could sit and enjoy the
day. I soon fell into a muse and turned to thinking of what had
inspired the Psalmist when he wrote: *The hills are clothed with
gladness... Let the sea resound and everything in it....Let the rivers clap their
hands...the mountains skip like lambs.* How true it was. Many times I
had watched the hills and observed the way clouds caressed them,
clothing them in majesty.

Many times I had witnessed their joyous response when cloud
chariots carried God over them sending rain to gladden the rivers.
How could all nature not know its Maker when he every day
multiplied the blessings he bestowed on it?

We passed close by wooded headlands above which thin
columns of smoke marked habitation and once we saw a boat
crossing a narrow sound between two small islands. Andrea got out
a chart given him by one of the Brei Oy monks and by early
afternoon we got a first sighting of our destination lying low on the
horizon. The sense of our excitement, though scarcely manifested,
was sensed by Argos who rose and went to the front of the boat
where he placed his forepaws on the gunnel and barked three times.
Even Miriam seemed to realise something was afoot, bleating a
joyous response. It made us all laugh.

As we drew near the island the wind fell away making it necessary to take up the oars in earnest. We could soon make out the topography which on first impressions looked barren indeed. All along the south coast the ground was low-lying and apparently marshy. There were tall reed-beds in places and several small streams running out of the foothills which were only lightly treed. We made for the south-east corner where the configuration of the land suggested a sheltered bay running in behind a headland. The ground was rocky, meaning there would be plenty of building material. Further north we could see the beginnings of cliffs behind which lay high open moorland. Another large island (we later discovered it was named Feide Oy, meaning Green Isle) lay to starboard at about five miles distance, its cliffs lit by the westering sun. A strong contrary current was moving in a south-westerly direction round the headland so we had no option but to make for shore with all possible speed before it carried us away.

After a short struggle we crossed into calmer waters and at once could see there was indeed a narrow bay behind the rocky outcrop. A considerable amount of driftwood lay piled along the coast here including spars and what looked like pieces of rigging. It was obviously an area where the conflicting currents gave up their bounty. A good place in which to at least make a temporary encampment. Rowing on into the narrow bay we shortly found a small pebbled beach on the starboard side and John steered us in.

We had arrived!

As soon as we landed and before unloading the boat, Father Andreas had us kneel together on the stony beach while he said a prayer in which he thanked God for delivering us safely and dedicated all our endeavours to the furtherance of His Kingdom. I looked at the grassy bank a few feet in front of me and thought how infinitely more desirable it would have been to kneel there. Yet I knew our prior purposefully set our knees on the unyielding and uneven surface of the beach in order that we might pray in pain, expecting us always to prefer suffering over pleasure and hardship over comfort. He would not allow us any complacency nor would he permit shirking. Monasticism was about to be imposed anew.

"We have reached this place by the grace of God," Father Andreas declared. "We will begin here. We will plant Christ's Church in yonder hollow and soon His holy name will be proclaimed to all men. *Deo volente.*

The day was far spent by the time we had everything unloaded and stacked on the bank. Our first priority was to make a temporary shelter and this we set about doing with a will. Thomas marked out a piece of ground in the shape of the boat and set the novices to gathering rocks. John and I went to help them while Thomas and Father Andreas began building a low wall, following the two converging curved lines. A gap was left in the centre on the lee side facing the shore. When the wall was at a uniform height of about two and a half feet, we began cutting bracken, laying it criss-cross to form a dry, even floor inside. Now we were ready for the roof which was to be none other than the upturned boat. It was heavy work requiring the combined energy of us all. When it was in position we stood back and admired our handiwork. Andreas pronounced it satisfactory.

"It will do for a few days," he said. "Get everything inside. I'm going to see if I can find some suitable rope amongst that washed up debris. We ought to lash the boat in place in case of wind. Come, Thomas, let's discover what else is over there. Some of those spars are going to require two men to carry them."

It was late by the time we finished. Stephanus milked the goat and we all enjoyed a refreshing drink with some of the bread our Brei Oy brothers had supplied. Immediately afterwards the prior recited Compline and we crawled into our somewhat draughty hut to sleep like the dead. There would be no Vigils this night.

The next day was Sunday. The prior read mass then delivered a short homily in which he spoke of the need for teamwork. He then gave each of us specific roles according to our talents and the traditional offices of monastic life. With so few to call upon and two of our number still novices, it was obvious we would each need to take on more than one task or accept that some things simply could not be done. On the previous evening Father Andreas had ceremonially placed the hourglass in Thomas' hands, declaring him to be our official timekeeper and responsible for calling us to prayers at the designated times. In regular monastic life, from Matins to Compline, all monks are called to pray seven times daily and to rise in the middle of the night for Vigils. All work stops and individuals either pray alone where they stand or more commonly gather together in the sanctuary.

Referring now to Thomas' responsibilities as timekeeper, Father Andreas added the role of Lector, meaning he would read (or more often recite) the prescribed lessons when called upon to do so. I glanced at John and saw he was smiling behind his hand. I could guess what he was thinking. Here we were, living under an upturned boat and our prior was dreaming of cloisters, choristers and cathedrals. Yet it was our calling and we must fulfil our obligations to the best of our ability.

John was next to be given his offices. He was to be our Infirmarian. Anyone who felt ill was to report to him. How Father Andreas knew to choose him for this duty I do not know but he could not have chosen better. John had healing hands and had acquired some skills as an apothecary's assistant in Iona. He was in possession of a box containing various medicinal concoctions and herbal cures, gifted to him by the Iona monks. In addition to this task he was appointed Barber and would be required to maintain our tonsures. This latter responsibility could hardly be considered onerous as the novices were not included.

I was to be Sacristan, having the safe-keeping of all our books along with vestments and vessels. Cyrus to assist me in this. I also had responsibility for provisioning with Stephanus appointed as assistant Cellarer. Though it was not said in so many words, it was understood I would be chief cook also. It was a hobby I enjoyed and if I was to be poisoned I preferred to administer the fatal dose myself. The others would have to take their chances. Both novices were to take turns milking the goat and the prior undertook to teach them how to make cheese. He would also see to their daily lessons.

For the rest we would work as a team applying our skills as best we could to create a harmonious and efficiently run community, ever mindful of the need to recruit converts and engage them to expand our enterprise.

"A year from now, *Deo volente,* we will have a flourishing community and Gjall will no longer be barren," Father Andreas said.

As no work was permitted on the Sabbath we spent the rest of the day in contemplation or attending prayers and in my case, going for a short walk in the afternoon. I was keen to explore the bluffs we had seen to the north. There were bound to be seabirds breeding in the vicinity. Perhaps some of their nests would be accessible. Stephanus and Cyrus asked if they might come with me and I readily agreed. The three of us, together with Argos, set off in high hopes of discovering something worthwhile.

As Argos and the boys ran ahead my thoughts turned to the tedious chore of tending the hourglass, given to Thomas. It occurred to me that in summer at least we ought to be able to divide our day by the sun. Even on cloudy days it was generally possible to discern where it was most of the time. At this time of year it circled the sky's rim like a tonsure; a little higher at the forehead (south) in the middle of the day and hidden briefly behind the back of the head (north) for a couple of hours either side of midnight. When fog obliterated everything we could resort once more to the hourglass but for the rest we could surely manage well enough. Before God had revealed himself to us through Christ, our forebears had worshipped the sun and the Celtic Church had wisely seen fit to incorporate the symbol in order to lure those sun-worshippers to the true sun; the light of the world. Marrying the old with the new made it easier to induce people to seek God and now it seemed to me more symbolic to mark our prayers by the sun's passage rather than by means of a man-made device. I would put it to the prior and see what he said.

A shout from Cyrus brought me out of my reverie.

"Come and look what we've found!"

He was high on the nearest bluff. Stephanus and the dog were nowhere to be seen.

"Have a care," I shouted as I hurried up the slope to see what all the excitement was about.

I was quite out of breath by the time I reached the top of the bluff where Cyrus was waiting for me.

"Where's Stephanus?"

"Down there"

It was another of those sloping grassy banks with sheer rock to either side.

"Look, there are puffins!" Cyrus cried excitedly.

And right enough a raft of them could be seen on the surface of the sea far below. Others were whirring in and out of their burrows near the cliff top either side of us.

"At the moment I'm more interested in what Stephanus thinks he's doing."

"He's looking for gulls eggs."

"It's the Sabbath, Cyrus, in case you've forgotten. And besides, climbing down cliffs without a rope is very dangerous. Show me whereabouts he is."

Cyrus pointed to a spot directly below our feet.

"See, there's Argos. He went down too. Stephanus is a little bit further along to the left, behind those big rocks."

"Shout down to him and tell him to come up at once. Tell him I said so."

"Yes, Father."

A short while later Stephanus' curly head appeared and he began clambering up with the dog at his heels.

"I could easily have got some eggs," he protested on reaching us.

"I don't doubt it. And how did you propose carrying them?"

This brought a lopsided grin.

"I hadn't thought of that."

"No, and you hadn't thought that collecting gull's eggs is no way to spend a Sabbath afternoon. You should be made to do penance."

This wiped the grin off his face.

"Sorry, Father. I forgot."

I relented.

"No harm is done. I think we might overlook it this time. Perhaps we'll bring a rope and basket and come again tomorrow. I think our prior is partial to gull's eggs."

On the way back Argos caught a young rabbit which he eagerly brought and laid at my feet. The wretched little corpse was still twitching though its eyes were wide and frozen in death. I could see the heavens reflected in one. A drop of bright blood fell from its nose, staining a leaf of grass. It was the Sabbath and sacrilege had been done. I felt my pulse quicken. Yet the dog had done no wrong. He had acted upon instinct. This was manna from heaven to him and he had gratefully picked it up – after a brief, if exhilarating chase. Our Lord had reaped corn and eaten it on the Sabbath. Might a dog not turn tail and become God for a moment? It was a Godly act to lay this food before me; sacrificing his hunger to feed mine – never mind that I had taken a vow to eat no red meat.

"He wants you to skin it for him," Cyrus said.

Trust a boy to see the truth!

"Then you do it."

"I don't know how."

I took my knife from the sheath which hung from my belt, judiciously avoiding looking at the small wooden cross that hung beside it. I had skinned many a rabbit as a boy. It was not so difficult when you knew how. Argos was sitting on his haunches watching me like a hawk, his tail slowly sweeping back and fore picking up bits of dry grass and thorns. Cyrus would have to comb it all out later.

When I had finished I handed the skin to Stephanus, furry side in.

"Peg it out, skin uppermost, where no animal or bird can get at it. When it is dry I will dress and stitch it to others, making you a hat for winter.

Stephanus beamed.

"Thank you, Father."

"What about me?"

"You'll get one too Cyrus, if Argos brings us enough rabbits."

"Is it right to skin rabbits on the Sabbath, Father?" Stephanus asked in an overly pious voice.

"No, it is not. However Argos must be fed and so I think, on this occasion, we may be forgiven."

I handed the rabbit to the dog, knowing full well it could have been kept unskinned until the next day. Argos accepted the meal with feverish tail-wagging then bounded off with it in his mouth. Unfortunately he went straight back to the boathouse where he lay down at the feet of Father Andreas and began noisily eating. I had no delusions or expectations of being dealt with as leniently as I had with the novices. An example would have to be made.

The call came the moment we were within earshot.

"A word, brother." And the prior beckoned me to him.

I avoided making eye contact with the novices.

"Put that rabbit skin somewhere out of sight," I whispered then went to my superior.

I will not go into all that was said. The memory of it still causes me to blush. Suffice to say I did penance. More to the point, I resolved to seek permission to begin my sequestration as soon as possible. I had decided it was to be for the duration of forty days and forty nights.

Chapter V

As long as it is day, I must do the work of Him who sent me.
Night is coming, when no one can work. **(John 9:4)**

During the following three days we worked through the sun's
compass, stopping only for prayers and for a few brief hours
sleep after Vespers before being dragged from our beds for Vigils in
the dead of night. Each new day began with Matins at sunrise which
at this latitude followed hot on the heels of Vigils. It was never-
ending.

Our first priority was to build a more substantial dwelling in
order that the boat might be returned to the sea in readiness for the
arrival of the Brei Oy brothers who were taking it back with them.
We did this by reinforcing the original wall and raising it another
two feet. The novices were then set to packing the gaps with smaller
stones and clay while the rest of us fetched the first of many spars
from the driftwood along the shore and began erecting rafters over
which we then added a turf roof.

One spar, longer and heavier than the others (which may have
been a mast at one time) was dragged to the brow of the hill above
our camp where Thomas fashioned it into a cross. Once erected, it
dominated the landscape in much the same way as the Celtic cross
had done on St Ninian's Isle. From this vantage point it was
possible to see a considerable distance and there appeared to be no
better place in which we could have encamped. There was fresh
water in a nearby stream, good shelter and ample building materials,
including the flotsam and jetsam which had already provided many
useful objects. In addition to these practical benefits we could not
have been more strategically placed to catch all interaction between
the several islands that formed this part of Thule. We very quickly

became a light on a hill and a valuable navigational aid to all our neighbours. Surely God had guided us.

Fresh water was an extremely important commodity. I have heard it said monks coined the saying *quod mundum est, deinde ad pietatem*, cleanliness is next to Godliness. It may be so. Certainly we are fastidious and thorough regarding ablutions, which is why I was so offended by the smell of the Brei Oy hermit. We considered our beautiful stream to be a Godsend and bathed in it regularly during the summer. In winter we broke ice on the surface to plunge gasping into one of its deeper pools. Better still, we found a spring of mineral water issuing out of the hillside near the hut and this became our main source of drinking water.

The walls and roof of what became known as the boathouse were finished on Tuesday morning, by which time I had also constructed an outdoor fireplace and clay oven which would eventually be incorporated into a small cookhouse. It was now time to mark out the foundations of more substantial living quarters – two beehive huts, a refectory and the all-important church which we planned to build on the brow of the hill alongside the cross.

Needless to say there was no time for collecting eggs though we dined well enough on fish caught by the novices in their brief spells of recreation. I managed to find time to make some oat bread which I achieved by wrapping dough round green sticks and rotating them over glowing coals. Our Brei Oy brothers had given us a skin of wine which we diluted with water. It was a most refreshing drink which, while far from being intoxicating, certainly invigorated our tired blood.

On the evening of the third day the prior announced his intention of taking a respite from heavy labour for a few days. We were all showing signs of wear and tear. John had crushed a finger when upending a rock. Thomas had injured his back and the novices were plainly exhausted. Thinking we were to have a rest, we were surprised to learn the plan entailed going on an expedition through the island, or rather up the west coast and back down the east. I estimated this would take three to four days, assuming the chart we had been given was a fair representation of what we might expect to encounter.

Father Andreas had obviously given the matter some thought as he proposed we meanwhile keep a lookout for two suitably isolated locations on opposite sides of the island in which John and I would simultaneously embark upon our eremitic retreats. He had in mind to develop what he termed a "compass of prayer" by enrolling our counterparts to the north to join us in simultaneous intercession.

"We will put a halo round the island out of which will emanate an aura of holiness," he said and it was apparent he believed this would create an atmosphere of such intensity as would create a positive response from the natives.

I was tempted to remind him that my personal aspiration was to temporarily withdraw from ecclesiastical mediation and from the role of being one of humanity's divine intermediaries and to spend time in solitary contemplation in hope of drawing nearer to God. Yet I could not find it in my heart to disappoint him so agreed to his plan. I supposed in the course of forty days and forty nights I ought to find time enough for both.

I wondered at how Thomas was supposed to make this journey as he was in no fit state to walk the distance. I need not have wasted a moment's thought on the problem. The prior (or God) had it all worked out. Thomas was to remain at home, with Cyrus and Argos to keep him company. This solved the problem of how the goat was to be milked. I had stupidly envisaged us leading the poor animal up hill and down dale.

We set off immediately after Matins at which Thomas had read the traditional Psalm. *O God, you are my God, I seek you, my soul thirsts for you; my flesh faints for you, as in a dry and weary land where there is no water* ... Except that the sky was threatening rain, the ground was sodden, and in any case Thomas wasn't coming.

Can you fathom the mysteries of God?

Job said it, not I.

To begin with the way along the south coast was dull and uninteresting as had been apparent when we first sighted it from the boat. The only place worthy of attention was the one we were drawn to that first day and the one we were now leaving. And as if to confirm the totality of dreariness, it began to rain. Yet we were committed to the venture and so plodded on regardless. Fortunately we were travelling light on the faithful assumption that *Deus providebit*. My particular prayer however was *di meliora:* heaven send us better times. Within an hour my prayer was answered. Better times lay round the corner; the corner being where we reached the west coast and turned north.

To either side of our island lay sea corridors that funnelled cold air to create mini climate zones. Between these a spine of low hills divided the weather as it passed north or south over us. Thus, while the rain headed up the east coast, we walked in glorious sunshine along the west. The landscape became infinitely more interesting as we progressed; the ground was firmer under foot and the aspect open and pleasing. Rolling hills sloped down to eyebrow curves of sand and shingle where oystercatchers piped strident warnings as they set about furtively attempting to decoy intruders on false trails.

After a couple of hours in which we saw little in the way of habitation, the shoreline began to rise and soon we were traversing cliff-tops with an ever-widening vista opening out before us. To our left stretched a channel of deep blue sea dotted with small green islands. Beyond it, at a distance of ten miles or so, the mainland of Thule pointed a long gnarled finger at jagged rocks standing in the Atlantic Ocean and marking the northern extremity of the archipelago. Ultima Thule, otherwise known as Iceland or the ends of the earth, lay over the horizon. On our crudely drawn chart of Gjall someone had playfully written "Here be dragons" to mark the region.

The sun was past its zenith when we came upon a spectacular area of cliffs in which large grass-topped rocks stood like tombstones in the graveyard of the sea. One, larger than the others and still connected to the cliff by a narrow land-bridge, appealed to

John as a likely place on which to establish his hermitage. I thought it a particularly lonely spot and very exposed to the north wind which in these parts was the coldest one had to endure. Father Andreas consulted the chart and concluded we were almost exactly halfway on our journey to the top of the island, making this the perfect place to establish the western side of his compass of prayer", provided a similar spot could be found for me in the east. The land bridge looked treacherous but that only served to convince John he had found his eyrie. There were to be no soft options.

Rather than explore the site, John requested that we not violate its sanctity at this time. He wanted to cross that land bridge alone and whatever confronted him by way of shelter and sustenance would be according to God's will. And so, having marked the spot on the chart, we continued north with the sun marching round its corresponding compass to arrive there before us.

Having already been given a clue as to where we would find the North Gjall monks, we easily recognised the wide curve of sand backed by high dunes. It was a wild treeless tract swept bare by the north wind. A truly awesome place in which to attempt putting down roots. Yet the brothers had obviously succeeded to date. Already there were a number of fine buildings scattered over a wide area. This had to be a sizable community. And so it proved to be; seventeen monks, ranging in age from three novices in their teens to a white-bearded patriarch who looked to be as old as the lichen-covered rocks.

The community had named their cell after Ninian which I thought rather unimaginative given that half the communities in Thule were so named. However, I reconsidered this view when told they possessed a relic in the form of a finger joint of the saint. When I conveyed the information to Father Andreas he showed considerable scepticism, having at one time been responsible for distribution of Ninian relics in Whithorn and claiming to know where they all were. Not that he was about to dispute the matter. Apart from being extremely impolite to do so, the prior explained to me that if a community *believed* they owned a relic then one should not undermine their faith.

"Faith is the substance of things hoped for," he said, quoting the New Testament book of Hebrews; although I was uncertain of what he was driving at given the context of the quote. Thereafter we always spoke of the community as "St Ninian's of the North".

We were given the warmest of welcomes and immediately bombarded with questions. It appeared our northern brothers received few travellers. Nor could they claim to have made any converts to date. When Father Andreas outlined his proposition of encircling the island with prayer, this met with an enthusiastic response. Everyone thought it a splendid idea. None of us were more than a generation away from superstitious susceptibility to earthly powers and all were keen to distance themselves from pagan rites and embrace the new order; or so we claimed.

Having discovered it only took a day to get from one end of the island to the other we spent the next three in the company of our nearer-than-we-had-expected neighbours, jokingly telling them they need not think of paying us a return visit for at least a year as we could offer no comparable hospitality.

While Father Andreas engaged with his counterpart and Stephanus went to explore the nearby cliffs with the local novices, John and I were taken on a conducted tour of the site by a middle-aged monk named Jerome. He was apparently the chief architect of all that had been done and was keen to show off his achievements. There were five one-roomed beehive huts, all with turf roofs. Each had a stone hearth in the middle of the floor. Smoke from the fires escaped through cone-shaped holes directly above. One of the huts was used as a kitchen. It had an elaborate fireplace with an oven underneath. I paid particular heed to the construction. Wooden pegs lined the rafters, each having a bundle of gutted and split fish hanging to be smoke-cured. Oily fat dripped from these bundles, making grease stains on the floor and occasionally landing on the heads of the unwary.

An ambitious work had begun on what was to be the church. (Jerome used the word cathedral but I thought that a little pretentious given the modest size of the foundations). Sandstone was being dressed and a mound of crushed shells had been gathered to provide lime for mortar. It was apparent there had been an earlier settlement on the site and previous stonework was being utilised. Sand and shingle pathways ran between the buildings and extensive walls were being built to provide enclosure for domestic animals and protect plants from the wind. Seaweed was being added to the sandy soil to improve it. For all that was being done in this regard I felt the relentlessly marauding north wind would thwart their best efforts. In this alone we had the better location and despite all the evidence of industrious endeavour, I believed our site had infinitely more potential for successful development.

Our sojourn was most enjoyable and relaxing. It was good to be part of a viable community and to share worship with a larger group. Hearing numbers of voices raised in song took me back to Iona and for the first time since leaving that wonderful community I realised how much I missed it. Yet I had set my hand to the plough in this particular furrow. I would not turn back. By the third day I was keen to return to our own little settlement and resume the challenge we had set ourselves. I was also eager to locate a suitable place to counterpoise John's chosen spot and thereby complete the halo of holiness Father Andreas wished to create.

Father Andreas spent some time re-drawing the island chart while we were at St Ninian's of the North, having made copious notes on the existing one. He had briefly studied cartography whilst in Rome and had a good eye for detail. He left the east coast of his new chart blank, aiming to fill in the details when we reached home.

Our return journey was both shorter and easier. It was evident the west side of the island bore the brunt of whatever Boreas hurled from the sky while the east was visited by a kinder god. There were fewer cliffs, softer hills and more trees. We saw our first sheep and cattle and passed several small settlements tucked into sheltered vales through which chortling streams ran out to the sea.

Though we saw both men and women going about their daily lives, none approached us or appeared to show any interest. I would have attempted to engage some in conversation however the prior was keen to try and reach our camp before nightfall and save communion for another day. I think he was conscious of a need to firmly implant ourselves before attempting to bear fruit. Besides, we were few in number and had no idea whether the natives, if aroused, might prove to be hostile. "Let sleeping dogs lie" seemed to be his motto, or perhaps it was a case of "fools rush in where angels fear to tread" and Father Andreas was no fool.

With the benefit of a more accurate chart it was possible to determine where we were in relationship to the west coast most of the time. Near the centre of the island the two sides converged to almost meet in the middle. This came about through two opposite arms of the sea reaching far inland to greet one another. It made the chart appear to be like an hourglass. I was hoping to find my particular eyrie in the vicinity as we were now more or less opposite John's. Thus, when we came upon the first real cliffs in several miles of otherwise flat coastline, I was delighted to see a similar configuration to that chosen by John. In time we would learn that these rock formations were referred to in the local tongue as "birriers". The word meant "sea-girt rock" and such places (of which there were many throughout the islands) would come to be much favoured by monks seeking a place of particular hermitage.

As soon as I set eyes upon the grass-topped rock I knew this was the spot for me and the others readily agreed it appeared perfect. In marking it on his chart the prior observed how it could not be more strategically located for the purpose of dividing his imaginary compass. At the autumn equinox, when we hoped to begin our sequestration, I would greet the first rays of the morning sun and John would bid it farewell in the evening.

Like John, I resisted the temptation to make further investigation of the site. It was enough to observe the narrow land-bridge that set it apart and imagine when the time came I might be the first to ever set foot there. I could only guess at what shelter might be afforded, whether there was a way down to the sea on the far side – none was observable on the landward side – and if there was fresh water available. There was a nearby loch though whether use of it was to be allowable was something I had yet to determine.

What were to be the terms of my eremitic sojourn? How strictly would I adhere to remaining on the rock? Would I allow some latitude, such as weekly baths in the loch for instance, or would that violate my self-imposed incarceration? These things would all have to be determined when the time came.

Meanwhile we were nearer to home than I had imagined and within little more than an hour reached the bluff where the puffins were and came in sight of the cross and boathouse. I asked Father Andreas if he had given any thought to naming our settlement and he expressed a preference for associating ourselves with one of the Gospel writers rather than a latter-day saint. In particular he favoured St John, claiming his was the most fully developed theology and therefore provided the best indicator to Christ's divinity. I did not feel qualified to express an opinion and when the prior said he would decide in consultation with Thomas, I was happy to accede to his wishes, feeling sure John would do likewise. And so we came to be known as The Holy Community of St John's by the Sea.

Chapter VI

***You can judge the quality of their faith from the way they behave.
Discipline is an index to doctrine.* (Tertullian)**

Argos came to meet us, his whole body wagging in joyous
recognition of his family. Cyrus was grinning from ear to ear
and I swear he was waggling too. Only Thomas maintained a
modicum of propriety though he embraced each of us in turn. One
would think we'd been gone a month.

Thomas' back was much improved and he declared himself
ready to resume work. In our absence Cyrus had explored the
surrounding district, finding nearby colonies of terns and kittiwakes.
Following my instructions he had taken one egg only from each
nest and had a basketful ready for me to cook. I could tell by the
expression on the prior's face that he thought I should make haste
and do so. I took the hint and in a short while we set about one of
the tastiest meals I had managed to prepare since our arrival on the
island. Knowing the season would be short we made the most of the
providence over the next few days.

And then the Brei Oy monks arrived. They came in a large boat
loaded to the gunnels. Ten men. A second, much smaller boat
attached by a short rope wallowed astern. It too was full of
provisions of every sort. As soon as we sighted them we piled leafy
branches on the fire, creating a smoke signal to indicate where we
were and sending Stephanus to the point of the ness to guide them
into the backwater.

What bounty! What generosity! Fresh cheeses, wine, honey, oat
and barley flour, salt, oil of two sorts, fresh and salted fish, a small
keg of spirits, dried fruits and more. There were fishing lines, rope,
candles and a tinderbox with spare flints, more tools, leather, tar, a
spindle and a bolt of cloth. Cyrus and Stephanus joined hands and

danced in a circle until Thomas thrust canvas buckets at them and sent them to the spring to fetch water. Then followed a tour of inspection in which we showed off our modest beginnings and outlined our plans. It was a joyous day, made more so by the promise of our Christian brothers to stay at least a week and help us turn The Holy Community of St John's by the Sea into a viable proposition.

It might be supposed that in all the ensuing activity I would forget my commitment to the forty day retreat and content myself in the business of waiting upon our guests, working the long daylight hours and praying. There was much to do and plenty to occupy my mind yet I can honestly say never an hour passed that I did not think of how it would be when I crossed the birrier land-bridge into peace and solitude. Many times in the midst of what was increasingly becoming routine monastic life I longed to set out on what I called my one-way journey to find God. Of course I fully intended to come back, but I would be a very different person when I did so. According to Luke's Gospel, when Jesus returned from the wilderness he did so in the power of the Spirit. He was a changed man. I too would be changed; of that much I was certain.

In the short time since our arrival in Thule the landscape had altered dramatically. The cliff-tops became clothed in dusky pink and every stream was flanked with yellow as earth put on its garland of wildflowers. Each passing breeze carried honeyed fragrance setting all the bees dizzy with joy. Even the mosses shone greener and every gull on every cliff ledge had its own miniature window-box of exquisite little flowers. Whenever I could reasonably do so I slipped away to the bluff for a few minutes alone. Below me was an amphitheatre full of action. Puffins, fulmars and guillemots crowded the terraces, squabbling over tenancy rights. And in the shadowed sea, porpoises sent schools of mackerel flashing and shivering in frenzied panic across the surface while already plump and gorged seals turned their languidly indifferent eyes skywards.

During the ten days in which our friends devoted their time to us everyone worked with such grit and determination that an astonishing amount was achieved. A purpose-built kitchen was completed along with two traditional bee-hive huts of equal standard to those at St Ninian's of the North. Work was begun on the church. It was not something that could be hurried. We all desired that it would be a representation of our best effort and therefore we must be patient. Our brothers promised to come again later in the year. It will be finished in time for the Feast of the Nativity one said, though I doubted it.

Two of our visitors left early one day. John went with them, the three walking one behind the other into the hills. They would not say where they were going. I pretended indifference then went straight to Cyrus and asked him if he knew what was going on. Cyrus, who was an orphan, had taken to following John like a puppy. I felt sure the father-figure would have confided in his adopted son. Cyrus merely shrugged. If he knew he wasn't telling. The men were gone all morning. I kept watching for their return when in truth I had better things to do.

Thomas called us to prayers at Sext. The company was gathered beside the cross listening to the familiar words being recited ... *O Lord, open thou my lips; and my mouth shall show forth thy praise* ... when I looked across the valley and saw our brothers returning, each one leading a sheep on a halter ... *Purge me with hyssop, and I shall be clean: wash me, and I shall be whiter than snow. Make me to hear joy and gladness* ... So that was what they were up to. Three monks gone to buy sheep. How had they known where to go? *Let the words of my mouth, and the meditation of my heart, be acceptable in thy sight, O Lord, my strength, and my redeemer.* I felt the prior's eyes upon me and bowed my head.

"I thought you were a fisherman, not a shepherd," I said to John later. "And why all the mystery?"

He brought his hands together as if in prayer – or to beg forgiveness.

"It was to be a surprise and we were unsure as to whether we would be successful. Are you annoyed with me?"

I laughed and shook my head. If he had asked was I peeved or jealous I would have had to lie. His preferring the company of others over mine was what had irked me. We monks are a strange breed. Touchy. Easily offended. We go to ridiculous lengths to justify ourselves. Sulk over trivialities then spend hours seeking God's forgiveness. We are forever *a fronte praecipitium a tergo lupi*, between a cliff and a wolf. Our problem is we never seem to know which is which.

The sheep were purchased in order that we could begin spinning yarn and weaving cloth. Self-sufficiency was important to us. With it came a sense of worth. Spending all day in prayer was a fine thing yet we needed to show the world that we understood there was more to life. And there was another thing about owning sheep, especially ones that would follow us out to green pastures and beside still waters. Though we would never admit it; sometimes monks like to play at being God.

When they departed, the Brei Oy monks left us their small boat as promised so that like the seals we too became plump and satiated with fish of every sort. It took a while to adjust to being a small brotherhood once more. I ought to have welcomed the feeling as being the precursor to a far greater solitude that awaited me. And I did; it just took a few days.

We were forever watching in the hope of seeing boats. Quite a few passed by going north to Feide Oy and beyond or south round our headland, yet none stopped. The word had not yet gone out that a welcome awaited all who turned aside from their journey.

And then the unexpected happened.

Stephanus and I were gathering seaweed, having discovered that the sheep liked to eat it, when we sighted a boat heading in our direction from the west.

"Run and put some green leaves on the fire," I said hoping we might catch their attention and cause them to pay us a visit. Our half-built church would be observable to anyone with a keen eye but it would depend upon their being interested or curious. Most of the natives seemed indifferent to our presence.

Stephanus scampered off to do my bidding while I kept watch; ready to direct the seafarers should they turn towards us. As the boat drew nearer I could make out three men, two plying the oars and one standing in the prow shading his eyes. They definitely appeared to be making a beeline for us. I glanced over my shoulder and saw that Stephanus had a good column of smoke rising to the heavens. I waved and the man in the prow waved back. He looked familiar. He *was* familiar. It was Leon! I saw him tap one of the rowers on the shoulder and when he turned I recognised Maccus. I saw now that they were aboard the same boat in which we had travelled from Orcades. I shouting a greeting and soon we were all together on the beach. The third man was one of the St Ninian's Isles monks; a man named Brendan whom I remembered meeting on that first day.

It transpired there had been a falling out amongst the community members. It was not uncommon. In most cases the persons involved claim to hold irreconcilably differing stances on matters of theology. In truth it is usually much simpler. Personality clashes are inevitable in monastic environments where men are deprived of the equalising effect of the opposite sex. The inflexibility of daily routine also tends to cramp the style of loners and monks, by definition, are first and foremost loners. The instinct to seek the life of a hermit is uppermost, yet realistically it cannot always be so. The monk needs his community as much as the community needs its monks. And thus some of us are constantly on the move, going from one monastery to another and never finding peace.

It does not do to probe; at least Father Andreas was not one to do so. I was less reticent, being of a naturally inquisitive nature. Little good it did me. Leon, whom I thought would be more forthcoming, gave the standard "theological differences" reply then clammed up. It hardly mattered. We needed extra hands to finish building our church and more to the point from my perspective, the chances of being freed to begin my retreat would be greatly enhanced if the prior found someone to step into my shoes. Leon was a good cook and Maccus had been Sacristan at Whithorn before leaving to come north. God was once again moving in his mysterious ways.

On the wherefore of their passage, Leon was more forthcoming and happy to give me the details. Once it was decided they were leaving, the Abbot kindly offered the boat and sent them off with his blessing. It may be supposed he'd rather lose a boat than keep a disgruntled monk – or three. The voyage had taken even longer than the one from Orcades and was not without mishap. Thule is a multifarious archipelago with many small islands scattered about like chickens round a long-necked and long-legged hen. Getting to Gjall involved sailing west, east, north, south and finally east again with innumerable convoluted meanderings in between. Twice they found themselves landlocked and had to double back; then a tide-rip carried them far out to sea where they became lost in fog, spending two days without food or water. The boat was unwieldy for so small a crew and none of them understood the intricacies of sailing. The wonder was they ever made it to our shore.

Brendan had been a weaver in a previous life on a remote island named Hirta which lay far out in the Atlantic Ocean northwest of Iona.

Could he make a loom?

Yes, he could.

And what about spinning?

Yes, he could do that too.

That clinched it. Brendan was welcome to stay as long as he pleased. The Abbot's only proviso (delivered with a wry smile) was that he probably ought to refrain from entering into "theological debate".

As for Leon and Maccus, we considered they belonged to us anyway. They were returned prodigals though they failed to qualify for a fatted calf. Father Andreas suggested they go and bathe in the stream and in the meantime I might like to bake a loaf of barley bread and we could open a pot of honey to celebrate their homecoming.

Before we knew it the summer solstice was upon us. We had enjoyed continuous daylight and now must prepare for darker nights. The symbol of lighting a lamp at Vespers seemed superfluous as did the opening line of the Psalm, *I call upon you, O Lord, come quickly to me.* Only in darkness did one feel God needed to be summoned. In daylight he was ever near. And rising for Vigils was no hardship. Those midnight hours were amongst the loveliest and many times I kept vigil all night long.

Yet it should not be supposed the weather was perpetually fine. Quite the contrary. Many a day we were enveloped in chilly sea fog and many others brought torrential rain or battering winds. At such times little work could be done. We stayed indoors and mended our fraying clothes and minded our fraying tempers. When opportunity allowed I enjoyed conversing with Leon who expressed great interest in what John and I were planning to do. He queried the wisdom of trying to endure forty days however, pointing out that to the best of his knowledge no one had ever survived longer than twenty. I explained that while I could not speak for John, it was my intention to temper things slightly. I would permit myself a morsel of food after Matins each morning while otherwise maintaining the fast. I considered water to be more important and would therefore drink a little three times a day.

"It is surely better to survive forty days and forty night of partial deprivation that to die after twenty of total abstinence."

Leon agreed.

"After all, I shall be totally alone the entire time and will be maintaining rigorous spiritual discipline in a confined space. Going entirely without food and water can only lead to such weakness of body and mind as to render me worthless for the purpose of knowing God, should he come. If I am not lucid then I am nothing."

Leon agreed.

"We do not propose beginning our vigil until after the autumn equinox by which time I fully expect to have to endure some extremely foul weather. The nights will be long and lonely. I admit to being a little afraid of the dark. I think Satan will come and torment me. I will have to be strong."

Leon agreed. He was a very agreeable fellow. How infinitely more congenial it would be if I could have his company for the duration. It was a foolish thought. One cannot be a true hermit in company with another. All of my life so far had been a preparation for what I was soon to undertake. I will have to be strong I repeated, except this time I said it in silence.

Chapter VII

And he said, Go forth and stand upon the mountain... and a
great and strong wind rent the mountains, and brake in pieces
the rocks before the Lord, but the Lord was not in the wind: and
after the wind an earthquake; but the Lord was not in the earthquake:
and after the earthquake a fire; but the Lord was not in the fire:
and after the fire a still small voice. **(1 Kings 19:11)**

The day finally came. A cold day. An indifferent day of blustery winds and intermittent rain. Not a day to begin a new venture. Not a day to induce feelings of boldness or self-assurance. A day that might easily bring doubt, second thoughts and (let's face it) downright terror. A momentous day nonetheless. Was I ready for this?

The prior had insisted upon us each taking one of the novices with us. Cyrus was to go with John and Stephanus with me. They would help carry our meagre possessions – a few scraps of inspirational reading material, extra clothes, a length of rope, candles, tinderbox and flint, a little salt, a small container of wine and bread in order to celebrate mass. We each had a canvas water bag and a clay pot in which to collect (and cook) shellfish or any other food we could find. We also had our knives and the small wooden cross that always hung from our belts. John gave me a small vial of foul-smelling brown liquid which he said would settle an upset stomach. That was all. No food. No small pot of honey squirreled away under our cloaks. No nuts, cheese or comfits of any sort. I had a length of fishing line but John did not. In fact we did not need any help to carry so little yet I think the prior wanted to be sure we arrived safely and he probably thought we'd be glad of the company along the way. Time enough to be alone when we reached our destinations.

The farewell gathering was depleted somewhat owing to Father Andreas having sent Thomas, Maccus and Brendan by boat to inform the St Ninian's of the North community that the proposed ring of prayer was about to be put in place. He obviously was placing great faith in the aura he believed would be created. In giving us his blessing and bidding us farewell, he suggested it would be perfectly in order if on arrival either of us wished to keep our novice for whatever was left of the day to help build a cell. They would need to return home before nightfall however. In making this concession it occurred to me that Andreas may in fact be hoping to learn a little about the nature of our chosen sites and thereby put his mind at ease. If he could be reassured that we were not putting our lives at risk, presumably he would sleep easier at night.

I looked at John.

"I think not," he said. "But thank you all the same."

I nodded in agreement. I was feeling strangely emotional and did not entirely trust my voice not to betray me.

"*Deus tecum*," the prior said. God go with you.

Ah, I thought, but it is I who go in search of him.

"And remember to enter upon the compass of prayer in which we will constantly be engaged."

I bit my tongue and said nothing. I would do as he asked but it was not my priority.

John was unusually subdued when we embraced before setting off for our opposite ends of the island. I tried to think of something appropriate to say. No thought surfaced other than trite banalities. It felt strange and unreal. A dream within which I was sleep-walking. Would I wake up shortly and go to feed the sheep? Or in getting there might I discover the birrier was a totally unsuitable place in which to set about my plan; after all, I had no way of knowing whether or not it was already inhabited. It could be a favourite fishing spot for some of the natives or a place in which they hunted seals. Worse still I might get cold feet when only halfway there.

Stephanus was in one of his chatterbox moods; delighted to be freed from his usual chores and determined to make the most of it. Poor boy. If he asked any questions I have no recollection of replying. Fortunately he was mostly talking out of a love of hearing his own voice and did not seem to notice my lack of response.

It was mid-morning when we set out and barely noon by the time we arrived at the birrier during most of which time it rained. Just my luck if I caught a chill and had to abandon the mission before properly beginning it. As if to confirm the likelihood, Stephanus sneezed. "God bless you."

I had said it automatically, despite having been told by the Abbot of Iona that to do so was superstitious nonsense. The notion that one's soul might flee the body – or as some would have it the devil enter – suggested a fragility of chance that could not be tolerated. What if one sneezed when no one was about to say the magic words? Half the world would be possessed and the other half mad from fear of it happening. Why, I might sneeze my head off alone on the birrier and be possessed by legions. When Stephanus sneezed a second time I decided to ignore it.

"Bless me, father," he pleaded.

"Fiddlesticks!" I replied and immediately regretted doing so when the boy's face crumpled in disbelief at my flippancy. I proceeded to explain the skewed theology but it was clear from the expression on his face that he did not believe me.

"Deus, non derelinquens nos," I said.

"What does that mean?"

"It is what the Bible teaches. God does not forsake us."

This seemed to pacify him and no more was said on the subject. If only all our doubts were as easily dispelled.

Stephanus was keen to stay and help me build a temporary shelter. I would dearly have liked him to do so but felt I'd made a silent pact with John. One thing was certain; John would not be allowing Cyrus to accompany him onto *his* birrier. I rather wished I had the same degree of unwavering determination as my friend. John would not yield to temptation; in fact, it worried me a little that he might be *too* obdurate. It would not surprise me to learn he had put himself in grave danger rather than acquiesce. His faith in God was much stronger than mine. The Devil would have no luck with John.

When it became clear that I was sending Stephanus straight home he begged me to at least allow him to cross the arch so that he could tell the others what the place was like. I could think of no reason to refuse him while at the same time wondering if Father Andreas had specifically instructed him accordingly. I did not like to ask and in any case doubted if he would be forthcoming.

"Very well," I said.

We held hands and cautiously edged our way along the narrow path. It was barely two feet wide and perhaps fifteen feet long spanning a sheer sided canyon. The sea was about eighty feet below us.

"Don't look down," I said, having already done so and been instantly overtaken by vertigo. The sea roiled and surged like a black serpent in its death throes. I could hear it being sucked in and out of a hidden cave and already began wondering what sorts of fearsome sounds were going to assail me in the dead of night undermining my courage and threatening my sanity.

Reaching the birrier we were faced with a steep climb up a precarious slope to the grassy top. Again I cautioned against looking down and this time took my own advice. To judge by the worn nature of the path I assumed animals of some sort must come this way from time to time. Sheep or goats possibly. I hoped it was none other.

The birrier was shaped rather like one of our beehive huts except that it was very much higher of course. For the greater part of the circumference the sides were more or less sheer. In one or two places it might have been possible to climb down with the aid of a rope. Even then it would have been dangerous to attempt it alone. As we proceeded on what amounted to a cursory tour of discovery I became increasingly concerned that I was to be stranded on what amounted to a high rock almost a furlong in diameter and totally devoid of vegetation other than close-cropped turf and the withered remains of summer's wildflowers. An ant on top of a pole might feel less isolated. At least the view ought to be impressive – if I ever got to see it.

When we reached the side facing Feide Oy it was with some relief that I discovered a wide section of the cliff had collapsed into a jumble of large rocks over which it was possible to climb down to the shoreline. The section amounted to almost a quarter of the compass and was bounded at either side by steep cliffs with no way round other than by taking to the sea. Somewhere amongst this field of boulders it might be possible to build a shelter of sorts although I could see nothing promising. It looked very exposed to the elements. However, at least I could get down to the sea and would therefore have access to shellfish, crabs, edible seaweed and presumably fish. A rather limited diet but probably adequate for survival nonetheless.

Returning to the top we began criss-crossing the short turf. It was featureless apart from a deep hollow near the centre which was partially filled with manageable sized stones and what looked like the remains of a wall. It occurred to me some sort of beacon or small watchtower may have existed here in the past. To judge from the way the stones had sunk into the ground and become partially overgrown, I concluded whatever the structure might once have been, it must have been long abandoned; quite possibly centuries earlier.

Up to this point Stephanus had tagged along beside me, saying nothing yet obviously taking it all in. I asked him what he thought.

"This is the place," he said. And then showing unexpected perception he proceeded to outline his assessment of its potential.

"If you move most of those stones and use your knife to dig out a circle of turf big enough to build a small cell down there in the middle, you can then build up the walls. There's bound to be some wood down near the sea that you can use to make a roof, in fact I saw one piece wedged between rocks. If you put turf on top it will be just like one of our houses at St John's."

He made it sound easy.

"Do you want me to stay and help, Father? I easily can."

"Thank you Stephanus, but no. I'll do a little at a time and hope the weather quickly improves to let me finish before any storms come."

I noticed a shelf of rock sticking out of the ground at an angle.

"Put my things under there and then off you go. I'll manage."

I was suddenly keen to be alone and would need all that was left of the day in order to establish a make-shift shelter to see me through the night.

"Come, I'll see you safely over the bridge then you must go straight home."

Home! What a comfortable and reassuring word that was. The companionable sound of voices, the warmth of the hearth and the smell of food (yes, I was already feeling hungry). How did I ever imagine I could do this?

When we reached the safety beyond the bridge Stephanus gave me an awkward embrace. There were tears in his eyes. He was usually so self-assured. I tended to forget how young he was.

"Off with you, and tell Father Andreas I'll be back in forty days."

It was meant to sound inconsequential. A joke. Unfortunately it sounded more like a life sentence. I could hardly believe I'd said it. What made it worse was the way Stephanus reacted. He took it like a slap in the face and I realised it was possible he was unaware of the finer details of the plan. It was not something that had been discussed much in the company of the novices. I patted the boy's shoulder.

"Go, and may God guard your safety."

I stood and watched the lad as he trudged along the grassy verge above a curve of pebbled beach. The rain had eased and a faint halo of diffused light low in the sky indicated the whereabouts of the sun. It would set in another three hours and at this time of year nightfall was never far behind, especially in a clouded sky. There was little enough time to make a start on building my cell. I ought to be getting on with it and yet I stood.

Stephanus began climbing the slope at the far end of the beach. He would shortly reach the crest and disappear from sight. I waited, hoping he would pause at the top and look back. Sure enough, he did. I waved and he waved back then turned and was gone. I felt a lump rise in my throat. This was not how it was meant to be. I ought to be feeling elated. Instead I felt bereft and totally overwhelmed by the enormity of what I was about to attempt. Forty days and forty nights! I needed to pull myself together. The first night was almost upon me and I was ill-prepared.

I hurried back to where my meagre possessions were stowed. The sight of them was comforting in a pathetic sort of way. These were to be my only links with the outside world for the duration. I picked up my roll of texts and kissed it. This alone ought to see me through. Feeling reassured I hurried off down to the outer end of my hermitage. If I could salvage a few pieces of timber I might be able to improvise something in the way of a lean-to. For the time being it would be best to do so down amongst the large boulders near the sea. I had no delusions of building a permanent shelter down there, as in stormy weather the entire area would be lashed by the sea – else how had driftwood been thrown so high amongst the rocks?

It took only a few minutes to find a cave-like niche between two enormous rocks. It needed a floor as the slope was all wrong. Stephanus had been right; there were several good spars and planks jammed between rocks here and there. Some were fifty paces or more above the high tide mark. Clearly it would be suicide to remain here in a storm. The sea would tear any living thing from its perch and dash it to smithereens amongst the rocks. Fortunately the wind was easing. I would be safe for one night at least. To the east, across the narrow sound, the cliffs of the Feide Oy were already becoming indistinguishable from the sky. It would soon be dark. Having a care not to stumble amongst the slippery rocks I managed to salvage sufficient timber to fashion a platform. I then fetched all my possessions and stowed them at the back of the niche where they would be kept dry. In the last glimmer of light I managed to prop a few boards in a vertical position at the entrance, lashing them together with some of my rope. It was a windbreak of sorts and would have to do.

The strenuous activity had speeded my heartbeat and heated my blood. More to the point it had occupied my mind, chasing out those irresolute thoughts and beginnings of doubts. I felt calmer. It was approaching the hour of Vespers; always a good time in a monastic community. The end of day when the cloak of darkness folds its shades about us. There is communion. There is a sense of things having been accomplished. Later, when we are alone in our cells, we might fear the absence of light and enter upon a brief period of reversal. Some of us may for a time be overcome by abject terror. A few lose their minds, though never for long and never to be admitted. Meanwhile I refused to dwell upon any of that. I love Vespers as a time of quietness; the sun has slipped away to rest a while and all earth has turned in upon itself seeking the balm and restorative unction of sleep.

This night I would not sleep. It was still too early for that. There was too much on my mind both in matters secular and spiritual; physical and mental. My mind was racing. My limbs twitched. Blood fizzed in my veins. Sleep was impossible. I would keep vigil and not be afraid.

How weak am I, O God? How far short of self-discipline? I did not even see the sun rise! It is true; I admit it. I slept the sleep of the dead. God forgive me.

It would be good to say I was refreshed and eager to greet the day. I was anything but. Cold woke me; cold and aching joints. All night the sea had pounded the rocks. Its rhythm had invaded my head, echoing and thumping in my brain. It hissed in my ears like a snake. My hair was plastered to my scalp. My face felt brittle. My tongue was coated with salt. I was hungry and thirsty. All that was needed to make my misery complete was for Satan to step before me and begin mocking.

I quickly opened my scroll which included several of the Psalms, randomly selecting the fortieth. *I waited patiently for the Lord … O my God, do not delay.* From beginning to end the words spoke to my heart. I read them a second time, out loud; shouting them to the stubborn foolish rocks and the uneasy sea. I had read this Psalm many times before yet never had it moved me as it did then. Every word seared upon my soul like a branding iron. I pledged to read the passage every day until God came.

I rose then and began to take stock of the situation. The sky remained overcast though for the time being it did not threaten more rain. Hunger gnawed at my belly. I had endured longer fasts, generally in times of total inactivity when all my focus was on contemplating theosophical matters. Now I needed energy to begin the task of building a more permanent shelter without which I could not hope to survive. And without food I could not hope to begin.

Fetching several small pieces of wood from amongst the rocks I took my knife and pared one into shavings. Tinderbox and flint got me a flame with which I first lighted a candle. Soon a small fire was burning cheerily. Next I searched along the ebb, finding an abundance of mussels. Collecting several I placed them unopened on the hot coals. When they sprang apart I prised out the flesh with the tip of my knife. The texture reminded me of fungi and the taste had the fragrant tang of the sea. If this was to be the extent of my eremitic withdrawal from the world it might not be so bad after all.

And so began an initial routine of prayer and labour not unlike the first days at St John's by the Sea. Each morning I fetched water from the loch across the way as there was none on the birrier. Aside from this I never left my eyrie. It took a few days before I was able to transfer my belongings from the rock niche to the newly built shelter at the centre of the mound. The walls were lower than a normal beehive house and the whole structure was much smaller. I made a poor job of the roof and lived in fear of it collapsing in a storm. The platform floor, which I transferred from the temporary shelter, was placed on a foundation of rocks to keep it drier. I even made a small alcove in which to keep my possessions and a recess for the candle. On the day I moved in I took a length of rope with me on the water-fetching journey to the loch where I'd noticed a thicket of tall reeds. Cutting a large bundle I dragged them across the rock bridge and up the precarious slope to the cell where I wove them into a passable sleeping mat.

It was the fifth day and the weather so far had been tolerable – just. I had kept to my predetermined plan of eating only a small amount of food each morning after Matins, varying between crab meat and mussels augmented by bearded lichen and seaweed both of which I knew to be edible and reasonably palatable when cooked together in the clay pot. A flat stone placed on top kept the steam in. Needless to say I was permanently hungry but I wasn't starving.

With the initial work finished the days became long and longer. My entire focus was now directed toward finding God. It was why I was there. I read my texts and recited passages of scripture I had committed to memory. I prayed. (I even remembered the prior's compass and conjured an image of us all joining hands round the island). To clear my head I walked round the perimeter of my little world, always going according to the path of the sun. To go contrariwise was to risk evil powers according to John whose fisherman traditions were deeply embedded in his psyche. He claimed scriptural precedents though I'd never been able to find any. Nevertheless I adhered to his advice. We monks frequently confuse superstition with the will of God despite constantly being admonished for doing so. In the midst of it all I looked for God in everything about me and most of all in my head.

The days were not so bad. Nights were worse. Waking out of troubled sleep and lighting a candle to banish darkness. Keeping Vigils. Keeping watch against the forces of evil and calling upon

God to send his guardian angels. All those prayers and recited Psalms. All those entreaties made in fevered anguish of unworthiness. Trembling in fear of what lay beyond the feeble circle of light that only served to deepen the darkness and hide the stars. Stars were my friends. Those pinheads of frosted radiance that spangled the sky, each one falling through the hourglass until it was empty and the pale luminosity of dawn filled the globe once more.

Vigils kept, I would snuff the candle knowing full well it represented Christ, the light of the world, yet it seemed to me when raising my tired eyes to heaven and seeing the stars once more that I had begun to resurrect the true light. Each star was a promise of light to come.

As the days stretched out and five became ten I many times wondered what folly had taken me to this place. Why should I, a humble penitent monk, sit alone on a sea-girt rock in the expectation of being visited by God when His Holiness, the Pope, sat in splendid opulence on St Peter's throne surrounded by all the trappings of decadence and supposedly held God in the palm of his hand?

Many extraneous thoughts began entering my head unbidden. There was neither rhyme nor reason to most of it and still less made any sense. At one point I began wondering about Paradise and how differing persons might have differing expectations – the Pope, for instance. Surely His Holiness would be content with nothing less than heaven as revealed to the Apostle John. After such a heavenly life on earth he would expect something unearthly of heaven. Yet I would be mortified (never mind I already was) if St Peter opened the pearly gates to me and invited me to tread streets of gold. Return me to earth, I'd plead, where I may walk the gentle, peaceful hills of Mull; see a more heavenly sunset than heaven knows and hear the euphonious song of a nightingale.

And what of Hell? Did Satan inflict degrees of torment according to one's sin? And in thinking such thoughts was I inadvertently inviting his response? Why should I become preoccupied with such things? Why did I care? The questions kept piling up. I became far more petrified of the prospect of having to confront the Devil than I had hope of seeing God. I was beginning to despair. I began thinking all my faith had been vicariously implanted by the communities in which I'd lived. Alone, I lacked the fortitude to hold on. Alone, I was assailed by doubt. And to think I had so recently wondered at the veracity of Thomas' commitment.

Though it was scarcely over five months since my arrival in Thule, I knew storms were a way of life in these parts; seriously horrendous storms that could last for days. It went without saying I would have to face at least a couple in a period of forty days and nights, especially when these days spanned the equinox; a time when the forces of nature battle one another for supremacy, ripping things apart in the process.

My first storm came on day seventeen when all my defences were down. I had newly fought off a foul sickness that tore out my bowels leaving me sweating on my pallet too weak to raise my head. I divided John's magic potion into two doses and took both; one after Matins and the other after Compline. Yes, the prayers went on. All of them longer than one would normally expect, though I admit they were more in the way of Job's laments than the psalmist's songs of joy. I wallowed in self-pity and the sun hid its face.

No food had passed my lips for two days. The very thought of shellfish raised bile in my throat. And in any case I was incapable of crawling to the cell's entrance let alone clambering over rocks to the sea where I would very probably have fallen in and drowned. To end my misery there and then would have been sweet relief. I admit it crossed my mind more than once. Satan was never far from my bed.

The storm came at noon. By midnight it had reached a howling crescendo, tearing at the earth, screaming round the cliffs and screeching in the caves. The very rocks trembled and the bruised sky haemorrhaged. My thoughts, such as they were, dwelt on Job. *The pillars of the heavens quake, aghast at his rebuke. By his power he churns up the sea ... I will teach you about the power of God ... Here is the fate he allots to the wicked … Terrors overtake him like a flood; a tempest snatches him away in the night.* Try as I might I could not conjure up the psalmist's lyrical assurances despite the two books lying side by side in the Vulgate. Job had turned the tables on his comforters and become mine. And he did it with God's complicity. The sensational spectacle was all God's. I lay quaking; expecting the roof to fall in and bury me. Someone would come at the end of forty days and find me already in my tomb.

Vigils require a candle. It was mockery to think of trying to light one however. Instead I groped for the elements of the Mass. Father Andreas had consecrated the bread and wine before giving them to me. I would find solace here. *Take this cup … This do in remembrance of me.* The wine soothed my spirit even as it soothed my tormented body. After Mass I lay down once more. The storm raged on. I remembered the prophet's words … *but the Lord was not in the storm* … Yet I knew he had answered Job out of a storm. Surely he was in all things. I would wait for morning and see … Deo volente.

The storm vanished in the pre-dawn hours leaving a pale anaemic sky for the sun to contend with. The entrance of my cell faced east making it possible for me to lie and watch sunrise. It was the first day I was able to observe it break free of the horizon unfettered by the usual tonsure of cloud that habitually ringed the sky. No longer committed to brightening my day it was now loathe to appear, sulking its way south at the extremity of the firmament where it could slip behind any passing cloud-curtain at will. In a few more weeks it would scarcely grace us with its presence. Six hours at the winter solstice, so I had been told, though one need not expect to actually *see* it. Was this a sign? Why look for the Son of God, the light of the world, when the world preferred darkness and the sun hid its face.

And with the storm gone would God now resort to an earthquake just to keep me guessing? Perhaps he would, though I doubted he'd manage to conjure up a fire in such a sodden environment. That left the still small voice. I was all ears – at least I was for a while longer.

My sickness and the storm had weakened my resolve. I would come to mark the eighteenth day as the nadir of my vigil and wonder if John was faring any better. His was the more exposed birrier. The storm, which had come out of the north, would have sorely tested a fortress never mind a monk's cell. Yet John was stronger than I. Many times I had observed his quiet determination to see through a task when others declared it impossible. John would win through, no matter what. I wished I could be as sure of myself.

I had not yet reached the halfway mark and was now having serious doubt about being able to finish the course. My head spun whenever I attempted to raise it. All my joints ached abominably. I was dehydrated and still nauseous, yet hunger prowled through me like a ravenous lion. If I lay any longer the crows would soon come and pick my bones. They'd make a poor feast of it. I was rapidly becoming skin and bones.

I thought of Elijah and how God had commanded ravens to bring him bread and meat. Send me a raven O God, I prayed. He sent me a starling instead. It flew in the doorway and landed beside my candle. I think the storm must have exhausted it. Without a second's thought I snatched and held it tightly in my hand. It blinked and opened its sharp beak in protest. I could feel a heartbeat under the feathers. Even a sparrow's fall is observed by the Lord, I thought. Yet a sparrow is not a meal while a starling is. Did he care about starlings? I hoped not and wrung the bird's neck.

Crawling forth, I managed to light a fire. No need to pluck the bird. I laid it in the coals and waited until all the feathers were burned then ate the tender flesh and sucked the bones. It tasted delicious. Miraculously revived I hobbled down to the rock bridge and crawled to the other side. After quenching my thirst at the loch I lay amongst the reeds, slowly recovering my strength. When I sat up a little while later the first thing that caught my eye was some wizened cranberries amongst a clump of heather. They were dry as currants but the intensified flavour was sweet to my tooth. Together with the roasted bird it was the best meal I had eaten in a week. God had not abandoned me.

On the next day I found a mushroom. It was the only thing I ate as I feared returning to shellfish too soon. On the day after I caught a small fish which I garnished with lichen after grilling it on the end of a stick. It was not enough. I had lost almost half my body weight and was beginning to wonder how I could go on. The whole exercise had ceased to be a theological one and had become a struggle for survival. I might play hide and seek with God and the Devil until Hell froze over and be none the wiser. In the meantime my body was wasting away. My joints were swollen and inflamed. My eyesight had become blurred and I was in mortal danger of falling off the cliff.

"Never mind the vision splendid, God. I'll settle for the still small voice."

I croaked it aloud, raising my face to the sky. All I got was an answering croak from a hooded crow that had come a little too close for comfort.

"Shoo! And that goes for you too, God!"

I was definitely becoming delirious.

Chapter VIII

The voice of him that crieth in the wilderness ... **(Isaiah 40:3)**

I woke to thick mist on the twenty-third morning. Sea wore it as a blanket and earth as a shroud. It crept into my cell, infesting every cranny and insinuating its way into my head. I felt sick to death, having eaten nothing for two days because I was still too afraid to risk shellfish and there was nothing else. I was at the end of my tether and too weak to care.

I heard a voice calling my name and a ghostly figure appeared from the direction of the bridge. It seemed to float across the ground. I thought I must be hallucinating and waited in fear and trepidation of what might happen next.

Stephanus materialised in front of me.

"Why didn't you answer, Father?" Then he appeared to realise the state I was in. "You look ill. Are you alright?"

I ignored the question.

"What brings you here? My vigil is for forty days. This is only the twenty-third. You have no right to be here."

"I know. Something has happened. You better sit down Father."

I was too weak to argue and lowered my aching body to the ground in some relief.

"Tell me."

Stephanus knotted his hands.

"It's Father John. He's missing. We fear he is dead."

"What makes you think so?"

"Cyrus had a dream two days ago. He was at heaven's gates and he met Father John who asked him what he was doing there. At first he thought he had died but when he woke up he realised it was Father John who had. He pleaded with Father Andreas to allow him to go and see if everything was alright. Father Andreas refused to begin with but Cyrus kept insisting something was wrong. In the end Father said we must both go but to leave Father John alone if we found him well."

"And?"

I spoke because he had ceased to. His lower lip quivered and anguish showed white in his knuckles.

"He was nowhere to be seen Father. We crossed by the narrow bridge. It is much more dangerous than the one here. We found his cell which is similar to yours only closer to the cliff face. It would be an extremely dangerous place in foul weather or in fog like this. Father John's belongings were all inside but there was no sign of him. Cyrus thought nothing was missing. We found no food or drink and we could see no evidence of any having been eaten. The cliffs are sheer on every side making it impossible to obtain seafood in the way you can here. It is a terrible place Father."

I was deeply shocked and confused. The news had numbed my senses. I felt sick to the core. Yet still I did not fully understand why Stephanus had come or why he had violated my sanctuary. He must have read my thought.

"You are to come home Father. Father Andreas says the vigil is over and he said to tell you he will not take no for an answer."

A fleeting smile crossed the boy's face and I imagined hearing the prior say the words.

"I have brought you food and drink. Father Andreas said you would likely be weak and must eat before setting out."

I wanted to argue. I wanted the boy to go back, state my case and on my behalf plead permission to stay. Yet already I could feel my resolve slipping away. Again Stephanus appeared to see inside my head.

"I have fresh bread and honey," he said.

The prior knew it was my favourite meal.

"I also have some diluted wine and an *apple*." This last was said with a note of triumph, as if Christ himself would not have refused an apple if the Devil had thought to offer it instead of all the kingdoms of the world. Who needs kingdoms when he's starving?

"An *apple*," I said in disbelief, noting that he had not yet produced anything. "How did you come by that?"

"We had visitors." He did not elaborate.

"And where are these things? I see no food."

"I left them beyond the bridge. Let me get your belongings and we will go. You must be starving."

It was then I realised how Stephanus had tested me. He had not violated the terms of my self-imposed deprivation, notwithstanding Father Andreas' instructions. He had allowed me to choose. The choice had always been mine and in weakness I made it.

Together we gathered up my meagre possessions and left the birrier. The fog was lifting as we did so. It was as if God might reveal his face at last - though he did not. Yet, I may be mistaken, for at that moment Stephanus appeared to be as good as God.

A Godsend, to be sure. And in any case, are we not all made in His image?

We sat at the beach while I ate. Twenty-three days had passed since Stephanus walked along this shore, pausing to wave at the top of the brow and I choked with emotion. What had been achieved? Nothing as far as I could tell and John dead in pursuit of it. I would suffer it all again and more if it could bring my brother back. Much later, I would come to realise that John had given his life to save mine. I had been nearer to death than I was prepared to admit at the time and with over two weeks still to endure it seemed unlikely I would have made it. A second bout of sickness was all it would have taken. There had to be a better way of finding God. Or there had to be a better man to do it.

Too often when intending to focus on my mission, my mind had wandered from the straight and narrow. I would find myself back in Mull; a boy at Christmastime when crisp and even snow lay round about and my mother read the shepherds' story, I sitting in the inglenook with one cheek cold and the other blazing. Then going next door to see a new born babe in a cradle and learning what swaddling clothes were; wanting to kneel and say an *Ave*, yet too shy to do so. Hearing my mother's voice as she went about our home singing psalms or at other times scolding the hens for coming into the kitchen searching for crumbs. Or I might wander down a summer's lane holding my father's hand while he, chewing a straw, told me about birds and bees, deliberately getting it all wrong and making me laugh. When eventually I returned to serious deliberation I would need to spend half an hour asking God's forgiveness. I was what my mother used to call a "broken reed".

The return to St John's by the Sea, which took three times as long as the outward journey, was painful in the extreme and not only in the physical sense. Each step became a torturous indictment on my presumptuous arrogance. A passage from the Psalms ran in my head: *When I consider thy heavens, the work of thy fingers, the moon and the stars, which thou hast ordained; what is man that thou art mindful of him? and the son of man that thou visitest him?* Had I misinterpreted this and presumed upon the sovereignty of God, thinking I could command his presence at will? Had the whole exercise been one of arrogant self-indulgence? And if so, was John's disappearance God's way of reminding me that humility comes before honour.

I had secretly imagined returning to the community as a conquering hero. Like Christ, I would be full of the Spirit. And unlike Christ, I would have boasted of having seen the Lord. Leaning on Stephanus, who indeed had become a little Christ to me as he practically carried my broken body; I vowed that from henceforth I would pursue humility, praying the merciful God would forgive all my transgressions.

There was to be no welcome home. All excepting the prior and Cyrus had gone to the west birrier to make a definitive search for any clue to John's disappearance. Cyrus would have gone too but the prior wisely forbade it. The boy had suffered enough.

In the days that followed I spoke at length with Father Andreas about all that had taken place. In truth much of it was confused and shrouded in the mist of uncertainty. I came to realise I must have been delirious some of the time. There were days I could not account for at all. The prior showed remarkable restraint in withholding all condemnation though he did say he hoped I'd learned my lesson. I think he must have known all along that the venture was doomed yet was wise enough to recognise my nature and that of John's. He would have known it was pointless to try and dissuade us. Like the Abbot of Thule in dealing with Leon and Maccus, it was better to let us go.

We held a Requiem Mass for John. He was my friend, my fellow-traveller from Iona. I thought I knew him best and imagined I loved him most yet clearly I was wrong. Cyrus was utterly bereft, as only a son who loses his father can be. And I could tell Father Andreas was deeply moved. He told me later that he had a special place in his heart for John and that for him The Holy Community of St John's by the Sea would ever after have a double meaning.

We never discovered what became of John. He simply vanished. In the end I persuaded myself that God had appeared out of the storm and taken him, like Elijah, up to heaven in a whirlwind.

In time I would come to realise that it is not enough to merely go through the set piece requirements of monastic life, whether alone or with others. One may pray all day long and fail to turn God's head if the prayer is not heartfelt. *Bene orasse est bene studuisse.* To have prayed well is to have pursued well. God will not be mocked.

Birriers would continue to be the preferred choice of eremitic withdrawal from society. My cell would be used many times and more monks would die. And sadly, history would think it reckless idiocy rather than rational endeavour. I still believe that wanting to see God is reasonable. He made us for himself and desires that we seek him. I asked Father Andreas what he thought and he said "*Spiritus est Dues, et qui in spiritu et veritate oportet adorare.* God is a spirit and we must worship him in spirit and in truth," which I didn't find particularly helpful.

And therefore, of all people, it was left to Thomas to have the last word.

"Blessed are they who have *not* seen and yet believed," he said.

Acknowledgements

In writing an historical piece of this sort it is important to avoid clichés and references that are not authentic to the period. In this regard I am indebted to a number of people who read the manuscript and made helpful suggestions. They include Rev David Cooper, Steven Fischer, Dr Tony Tymms, my sister-in-law, Hilary and my brother, Bjorn. I thank each and every one of them. Any remaining errors are entirely my own.

BY THE SAME AUTHOR

The Ninian Plate

Alastair Christie-Johnston

A5, 186pp. Paperback £8.99.

ISBN 978-1-904746-73-7

Ebook: Available for Kindle from Amazon

AD 603 "We call it the Ninian Plate…It is said to have miraculous properties. In its many voyages it has protected men in the boat in which it has travelled…It gives protection from danger to any who carry it and through them, healing to others…"

The Vikings came shortly after Beltane. They came before dawn under cover of a sea fog. They came swiftly and silently and with single-minded intent. No one saw them coming.

"Take this," he said, tucking the community's most prized possession in behind the baby. Better that the woman should have its protection, even if those left behind were exposed to greater peril as a consequence…

AD 2000 "…I know it's there. Try the loft or boatshed. The design work will be readily recognisable from the photos of the other Ninian's Isle artefacts. Remember, we're talking big money. Keep an eye out for Maunsie; he seems to have got wind of it – been asking leading questions…"

From the day the Ninian Plate arrived in Shetland it brought strange and terrible events into the lives of all who touched it. Where will it end and who will be the next to come under its influence?